Adventure in Jade

AMERICAN JADE

ADVENTURE IN JADE

JAMES LEWIS KRAFT

NEW YORK: HENRY HOLT AND COMPANY

PRINTED IN THE UNITED STATES OF AMERICA

This book is for

PAULINE KRAFT

whose patience with her husband's time-consuming hobby is enduring; whose forbearance is surely beyond that of all other women; and whose jewel box contains, if not the richest gems in the kingdom, certainly those wrought with the greatest affection.

Contents

ACKNOWLEDGMENTS

To THE MANY PEOPLE in all parts of the country who have contributed fact or fancy, clue or key to sources of jade on this continent, my sincerest thanks are due.

I should like especially to thank the man who first sent me a piece of North American jade, my friend Homer Leash, whose ninety pounds of Queen Charlotte Islands jade started me off on my adventure; and Frank Bacon, the prospector who found the Chan jade claim for me, thereby giving me a whole mountain of jewels.

To W. G. Bailey, editor of the Siskiyou *Daily Times*, and R. T. Fero, of the same county, go my thanks for digging into much history of early California to ferret out the tale of Chan.

To James Robbins, who has done so much to uncover the mystery of jade sources in Alaska and who has supplied me with many a wonderful yarn and fine piece of jade of the north country;

To Allan Branham, who never lost faith in the jade of Wyoming and whose dearest dreams have come to reality;

To discoverers of jade in many sections of this country who have generously shared their knowledge and their jade with me—

My thanks. Some of these are mentioned by name in the pages which follow; others too numerous to list share in my debt of gratitude.

With deep appreciation I gratefully acknowledge the very able assistance of Imogene Powell Frost, without whose encouragement and co-operation this book would not have been written.

Last, but by no means least, I want to thank Orr Goodson of the Chicago Natural History Museum whose careful scientific scrutiny and classification have identified the new great jade finds of America as truly nephrite jade.

All those to whom my thanks are due have taken their satisfaction, not so much in becoming a part of the record of an exciting hunt, but in being privileged to know jade in the first place. If contributors to the subject matter of this book and I, their chronicler, when we are done, have made rockhounds of some score of newcomers to a fascinating hobby, we shall all have been amply rewarded.

Benign and sorrowful
Confucius plays on the singing stones
On the stones of many-colored jade:
Plume-of-the-fisher-bird
Old-red-of-cinnabar
Green-of-the-melon-peel
Sky-after-the-rain—
These are the colors of which his song is made.

The purple of jade for compassion
The red of jade for love
Green that the earth may flower
Blue for the peace of the heavens.

Benign and alone Confucius plays
On the jade of many colors
And one who passes by far off listens and intones:
"Full is the heart of him who plays the singing stones."

—IMOGENE POWELL FROST

The title of this poem is the Chinese symbol yu.

1

How a Hobby Began

IT'S A STRANGE THING about a hobby: a man starts off on one, jogging along at a comfortable pace, and before he knows it, somebody points a finger at him and says, "Now look who's riding!" Of course, it's always the hobby riding the man. All the same, I know of no pleasanter labor.

There is scarcely ever any accounting for the steed a man is borne by and ultimately bears as his hobby. I don't know that it makes any difference. Stamps, porcelains, chessmen, three-tined forks, or buttons—all of these and millions more seem to have their peculiar fascinations. They have their riders, disciples, apostles, and devoted slaves.

Now a "hobby" originally, in medieval days, was a special kind of small, trotting horse from Ireland—a capricious, deplorably stubborn, fancifully Gaelic horse, capable of prodigious labors when the spirit moved. It had heart and wind and a mind of its own, and it carried its rider to any enchanted land of its choice. I am not sure that it wasn't the exclusive steed of the "little people," kicking up its heels and laughing at the sober drudgery of less imaginative dobbins plowing the fields. At any rate, this is the kind of mount a hobbyist rides to this day.

The beautifully caparisoned, five-gaited steeds which your true collector mounts are horses of a different color and character altogether, much more suited to the show ring. Collectors as a rule accumulate things because they have great rarity, and hence value for other men. A hobbyist collects what may have value for him alone. As a rule, a collector is a monied man, his pride in his collection partly, at least, derived from the cost of the objects in his museum. A good hobby can be—and frequently is—as near as your right hand and free as the air you breathe. (Of course, even the humblest hobby can be in time just as expensive as you like. And a hobbyist can be both collector and hobbyist. But if you are to be both, you must keep horses in both stables—the hobby for traveling, the show horse for the ring.)

We all start out in life enthusiastic riders of hobbies. If you doubt the truth of this, all you need do is examine the bulging pockets of any small boy. What will you find in addition to the pocketknife, the top string, the presidential campaign button or two? You will find stones—common, beautiful stones, water-washed pebbles if the boy lives near the sea, chips of quartz or agate or any fascinating thing brought to the boy's attention along roadside or open field.

Stones—just the common stumbling, bumbling stones all about us, ripped in great mountain convulsions, pounded out by the sea, patiently prepared by wind and rain and storm, scattered along everybody's path wherever he lives—stones are almost everyone's first hobby. Even the baby learning to crawl picks them up—and likely as not puts them in his mouth for safekeeping.

As they are a first and natural hobby, I cannot see but that they should be the last, the ultimate hobby of man. Nothing else in or on the earth is so ancient, so various, so mysterious, so beautiful. Nothing is so closely bound up with man's age-old efforts to know himself and to master his environment. From the Chinese jade adze of the Stone Age to the emerald-cut diamond of today, stone has told the history of man, as well as all the geologic history of the earth from the beginning of time.

How a Hobby Began

But when my hobbying with stones began, no such pro-
fundities cluttered my youthful enthusiasm. I was simply
plowing our east pasture on a small Canadian farm. Like most
everyone who helped to cut new prairie on this great continent,
I used an old Moline hand-guided plow—the type that works
calluses on your hands, but is slow enough to allow plenty of
leeway for the imagination, plenty of time to pick up over-
turned rocks that strike your fancy or arrowheads dropped
long ago by earlier Americans.

In making my childhood collection, I perhaps had something of an advantage over many boys and girls. For up to the
time when I was about fourteen, I had been unable to dis-
tinguish objects clearly. Nearsightedness was so acute and so
distressing that I assumed everyone on earth suffered con-
tinuously from furious headaches, and that all the earth had
the blurry image of a boat seen from under water.

Then a great wonder-worker magically gave me back the
earth and all that was in it, completely in focus and beautiful
beyond anything I could have dreamed. He was a homely
magician, a kindly eye doctor who came to spend his summers
on the shore of Lake Erie. He watched me as I tended his horse
and washed his buggy.

"Lew," he said "you're going over to Buffalo tomorrow and
get fitted for a pair of spectacles!" But in a home with eleven
crowding children, and the inevitable equally crowding mort-
gage, I could see no money for glasses.

The magician supplied the glasses. I cannot think of another
act of human kindness during my lifetime which can compare
with his—and I have tried to make a study of human kindness.
The look of the hills, the road, the streams, even of the people
who, as they walked, took on definite lines instead of a blur—
the wonder of a world in focus—is something I shall never be
able to get from eyes.

So plowing the east pasture with my new eyes wide open, I

began the treasure hunt that has led me to a lifetime of adventure, an eternity of pleasure, an occupation of hand and heart and spirit that has never left me for a moment.

The early chips of agate and quartz, the Indian arrowheads and other treasures of unspeakable worth which I uncovered, I hid beneath our front porch. For my mother, a gentle but much harassed Mennonite, was distinctly an enemy of clutter and small-boy accumulation. Busied as she was by a growing family, she could not be otherwise.

And as a matter of fact, women, with but few exceptions, seldom become great hobbyists. They are by nature too neat, their dust brooms too swift. Of course, there are exceptions. And often they make splendid collectors, for cataloguing and furbishing and showing to advantage a collection of things intrinsically capable of being put in order seem to come to them naturally. Whatnots were invented for the use of women— cubbyholes for men! True hobbies are apt to be cluttery, disjointed, even messy. Get a basement workshop all your own if you have a hobby—or at any rate, get a large open front porch.

My stone hobby led me along many curious paths through the years. Indian-fashioned arrowheads, the primitive axes and tools and stone bowls of ancient history in America for a time occupied almost all my interest.

Later, the stone of pre-Indian life took hold on my imagination, and I pursued fossil fishes wherever I could find them. Occasionally near my father's farm on Split Rock Hill I found a fossil fish among the limestone deposits. Even later sorties took me to the fossil diggings of Wyoming and other sections of the West.

Most of my early treasures among these stones I managed to salvage and have to this day in a small log museum, joined and fitted after the Finnish fashion, at my summer home in northern Wisconsin. Visitors sometimes like to see them. But for me each one represents the trophy of a thrilling adventure. Billy the Kid did not look at the notches in his belt with more elemental pleasure than I surveying this accumulation of a lifetime.

From the archaeological objects of America, my hobby pranced off quite naturally, it seems to me, to the stone-written records of other days and peoples. Babylonian and Syrian artifacts, telling tales some six thousand years old, had, and still have, a curious fascination for me. At one post change on the hobby road, I picked up a Babylonian cylinder telling the life story of Nebuchadnezzar. It still seems to me as contemporary as today's newspaper and rather more moving.

To become interested in the stone-written records of the valley of the Nile, of the Near East and the Far, is to become interested in the whole subject of ancient seals—eventually Chinese seals. Much of man's history is dated from seals. It would appear that from the earliest record of man's doings, all nations with any semblance of civilization used them. The sacred nature of these written promises or signatures or records of power is indicated by many Biblical references and by everything else that authenticates for us the ways in which ancient men thought and conducted themselves.

Thus inevitably, searching among prehistoric stone records, I came into possession of some Chinese seals—jade seals of the sort that have added much to known history and fixed the date of the Chinese dynasties from the beginning. Though among my Chinese seals are many exquisite carved pieces of lapis, agate, and chalcedony, the jade seals from the first appealed to me most, both for their intrinsic beauty and for the long culture they represented.

It is quite likely, historians tell us, that the first of all the world's written history is recorded in the jade pieces of ancient China. Its earliest rituals for worshiping one God are told in the tomb pieces of that land. And all that we shall ever know, very likely, of man's earliest great culture is told in the votive and ceremonial jade pieces which come down to us from a time otherwise unrecorded.

Adventure in Jade

In my collector's stable I am fortunate enough to have one of these very early ceremonial pieces: the jade buckle of a high priest. It belongs to the Babylonian period of 2600 B.C. and is beautifully carved of pale milky-green jadeite. It was carved most probably in China, brought to Babylon, and purchased by the high priest of the Moon-god Sin, whose name means God of the homes, tents, or reeds. Its story is told in an engraving on the central bar. Identified and translated by scholars of the University Museum, Philadelphia, the priestly buckle reads: "This buckle is presented with the word of Kuishtaah, servant of Enzupi, high priest of the God Sin in the Ekua Temple." It came to me through my friend Fahim Kouchakji, owner of the famed Chalice of Antioch.

Much later along the hobby road—though these, too, belong to the collector's mounts—I was fortunate enough to come by some extremely rare and beautiful carved jade pieces of the classic age of China. Nothing ever created by man out of the material of this world sings so eloquently the artistry to which he can attain or the heights to which his imagination can soar. I have a white jade teapot with cups to match which is surely one of the most beautiful objects in the world—thin as a butterfly's wing, delicate as the finest lace.

Through the years, pursuing my hobby wherever it led me, I have always tried to meet friends along the road, to seek out men with similar interests, to write to them and know them, and to travel along the way with them as far as our mounts chose to trot together.

Among these friends the word got around, as such things do, that I was interested in jade. One day back in the twenties, a friend from Alert Bay, British Columbia, sent me a large and interesting package containing a number of Haidan Indian artifacts. In the box were several objects of dark green jade: an adze; a few half-formed cutting tools; a kidney-shaped piece weighing about ten pounds, entirely uncut.

[6]

How a Hobby Began

The stone itself was beautiful, smooth, and cold, as is ever the way of jade. I put the uncut piece on my desk at the office where I could look at it and feel its dark cool smoothness and speculate about it. Up to that time, scarcely a scholar in the world was so rash as to suggest that jade, the stone of mystery all over the earth's surface, was indigenous to this continent. None had ever been found here in situ. None, to the scholar's knowledge, had been found in float. As a matter of fact, the original sources of jade have been obscure even in China, the place where jade has always been most used, most highly prized, and best known.

An omnivorous reader of everything I could get my hands on concerning the work of American Indians from Alaska to South America, I had often come upon references to jade amulets and axes and carved jade pebbles found in Alaska and in the ruins of ancient civilizations of the Aztecs and the Mayas to the south. The scholars insisted that these jade pieces came originally from the Orient, transported by Orientals across the Bering Strait and brought by barter and trade from Alaska to the southernmost tribes. More imaginative writers sometimes speculated about the lost Atlantis as a possible source of the world's early jade, including that of the Chinese.

So tantalizing were the references to the jade artifacts in America and so fascinating were the jade objects from this continent which came to my hand that I began to sense a mystery much deeper than the scholars hinted. If so much jade, both cut and uncut, had been found in the ruins of our earliest civilizations here, was it not reasonable to suppose that the raw material, at least at one time, was right at hand, afloat in our streams, deep in our mountains—especially in our young mountains, the great Rockies, only newly upheaved from the depths of the sea? I expressed this view to some of my scientific friends, but most of them, while kindly disposed and indulgent, said they hardly supposed my theory would be borne out in fact, since it had not been borne out already.

[7]

I decided to find out for myself, if I could. Furthermore, since I was no longer content merely to look at the outside of stones but wished to discover the beauty locked up within them, I became a rockhound and a lapidary.

It came about this way. One day as I was driving east on the Columbia River highway, near the spectacular Bridal Veil Falls, I saw a group of people—eight or ten of them—halfway up the mountainside, digging into the rock formation with iron picks. Each member of the party carried a canvas bag or knapsack strapped over his shoulder.

"What are those people doing up there on the side of that hill?" I asked the friend who was driving me.

He laughed and said, "Why, they're rockhounds! The hills around here are full of them!"

"What are rockhounds?" I asked.

Then he explained: "These particular rockhounds belong to the Oregon Society of Amateur Laps. They are out looking for gem stones. When—and if—they find them, they will take them home, and cut and polish them and make jewels out of them."

"Stop the car!" I said. And leaving my friend to wonder what had gotten into me, I scrambled up the steep hill as fast as I could. With true rockhound camaraderie, they received me graciously. And with the enthusiasm of the breed, they explained what they were doing and gave me the address of a man in Portland who could supply me with some equipment to follow through in cutting and polishing gem stones.

I have visited with all sorts of rockhounds, amateur laps, and societies for adventuring among stones since that time—and more diverse and interesting people were never banded together by a single absorbing interest, I feel sure. There are thousands who rejoice to be known as rockhounds throughout the United States. Rockhounds, may your tribe increase!

So from rocks—just plain stone—through many a devious path I came back to rocks. Specifically, after many a journey

and sortie, I came to one special kind of stone: jade. If this
seems to be cutting things rather too thin, I can only say that
pursuing jade on this continent, working with it, coming to
know it, satisfies every requirement of my hobby-riding nature.

I believe jade to be the most various and beautiful of all the
stones of earth. I believe the mystery of its sources on this
continent is one of the most challenging to the adventurer.
And I believe that anyone with salt and leaven in his soul can
ride this hobby right up to the pounding blue of the Pacific,
uncovering many a treasure on the way.

There is jade—a vast plenty of jade—on this continent, both
in float and in place. There is jade for the finding and the
working—jade of a vastness and beauty as yet undreamed. Some
of my adventures with it have been of the armchair variety,
some in the nature of explorations, some in workshop labor.
All have led me to the conclusion that jade is the perfect hobby
—for me. These chapters, relating some scattered experience
along the way, will attempt to show why.

2

What Is Jade?

IF YOU ARE to understand the unique and wonderful excitement of adventuring with jade on this continent, you will have to go back with me to an armchair consideration of jade in an older world. You should even take a brief glance at the nature of all gem stones. I do not like to delay getting at the heart of the mystery, but something about jade makes the mystery worth uncovering.

All precious, semiprecious, and common stones have their own charms for somebody—the woman whom they adorn, the potentate measuring power in terms of rubies, the geologist, the jewel dealer trafficking in what is rare and fashionable. That exclusive order of minerals, the precious stones, sternly limited to diamond, ruby, sapphire, and emerald, have a value so long fixed in the public mind and in the market place that there is no disputing their eminence.

To the limit of their purses, collectors may acquire these—and welcome. They are not for the hobbyist, and they are not for me. Beautiful as they are and eternally valuable everywhere, but fixed in that value, they are to a rockhound something like a tankful of exotic fish in an aquarium to a veteran fisherman. He admires the prizes in their cages, but give him a rod and a line and the most unlikely stream.

The world of precious stones is very largely charted country. Discovery in the field leads to well-marked paths of commerce and adornment and museum; and there is no charm whatsoever in it for the finder, except possibly those great pots of gold which have always in some quarters proved sufficient reward. Even gold itself, a naturally quite beautiful and harmless mineral, has ceased to have its original charm for the same reason. The precious stones, gold, silver, wampum, or any coin of the realm have got mixed up with man's daily living to such an extent that they are virtually worthless to him in the pure realms of the spirit.

With the semiprecious stones it is not so. These are worth whatever value a man may care to put on them. Most men do not specially covet agate, moonstone, chrysoprase, smithsonite, beryl, opal; yet among these and thousands of others are beauties not touched by those haughty aristocrats of the earth's crust—diamond, sapphire, ruby, and emerald.

In the first place, there is one outstanding quality which gives a stone the right to be known as precious. Clarity, brilliance, and color are all factors. But the nub of their preciousness is this: hardness, simple hardness. The greatest aristocrat of them all in this particular, the diamond, has a hardness of 10. And all other stones, precious and semiprecious, are measured by its scale. They all fall short, but only a little. To endure, and therefore to be precious, any stone must withstand the ravages of common dust, that insatiable devourer of all matter. For dust is filled with quartz particles, and quartz, being a gypsy among stones, is present everywhere in the earth's crust. Quartz is undoubtedly the abrasive in the mills of the gods which grind so slowly, yet so exceeding small.

Most of the semiprecious stones being softer than diamond, endure less long, alter their physical natures more quickly, return to dust faster, and hence do not stand up so well in the actuarial statistics of the jeweler and the connoisseur.

This limited mortality of countless fabulously beautiful stones is what keeps them in the class of semiprecious, not precious, stones. But among semiprecious stones there is one notable exception; that stone is jade. Though the precious stones are harder, jade is perhaps the toughest stone on earth. Furiously integrated as it was during pre-Cambrian times, when the earth's boiling point was presumably rather low, its resistance to being broken or crushed is something wonderful to behold. Like the meek, and for the same reasons, it inherits the earth, and comes as near to being immortal as the stuff of earth can be.

In many ways jade possesses a peculiar fascination for the armchair explorer, the rockhound, the prospector, and the man with a diamond saw and polishing machine. This is the beginning of it: jade in its physical properties is unique. It possesses a oneness of composition; it has no easy lines of cleavage, but when destroyed, splinters into fractions. No wonder the Chinese considered and still consider jade the stone possessing the cardinal virtues whose embodiment is truth.

You have only to look at a piece of jade—better still, hold it in your hand—to learn why this semiprecious stone, never valued very highly in the money marts in its uncut state, has to millions of people through ages of time been the peer of all jewels on earth.

Here is an anomaly: there is no such mineral as jade. And here is another: this continent, which up to our own time was thought to have no jade at all within its great mountains, gave the aggregates of minerals known as jade their name in the first place.

Basically, there are two minerals entitled to bear the name jade. They are jadeite and nephrite, and they belong to different mineral groups. Nephrite is a variety of amphibole; jadeite is a member of the pyroxene group of minerals. Jadeite is a silicate of aluminum and sodium. Nephrite is a calcium and magnesium silicate. Both minerals crystallize in the monoclinic system, but crystals of either are exceedingly rare. Of the two minerals, jadeite is a fraction the harder, but nephrite is even more resistant to destruction. Both were formed under very great pressure when the hearts of mountains were filled with heat and a singular passion for beauty.

Still another mineral, chloromelanite, is entitled to wear the proud name of jade, though it is so rarely found—and is of such priceless value when found—that it is seldom even mentioned in the listings. Vesuvianite or californite is listed by some authorities as jade, as are a few other minerals. But though many of them are extremely jadelike and often very beautiful in their own right, I think they must be omitted from the purist's scale of jades. The Chinese, to whom jade is sacred, are rather irritated by any jade impostor—for their own use, that is. But so long as the pretenders are called what they are, and do not ask for any crown greater than their own, I like them and work with them and find them beautiful enough. I just don't call them jade.

Call jadeite a composition of aluminum and sodium if you like, and nephrite a composition of calcium and magnesium if you will. But you have no more described jade than if you had attempted to list a man's qualifications for Who's Who by reciting the minerals of his body.

Study the inward patterns of jade through a microscope, however, and you will begin to see the curious and wonderful character of these stones. You will find nephrite jades to be in fibrous patterns which are arranged in most intricate designs, parallel, tufted, or fan-shaped. These patterns—whorled, curved, twisted, integrated, interlocked, and shading from one tone to another like a living branch—were surely the original inspiration of the great Chinese carvers. They regularly carved their beautiful vases, ornaments, and articles for worship to suit these inward designs of the stone itself. A piece of jade shading from green to yellow would inspire a tree branch with a yellow butterfly poised lightly on it, all carved from the same piece. They suited their pattern to their cloth.

Equally fascinating in design is jadeite, its structure being either granular or fibrous, the former being somewhat more common. Individual grains seen through a microscope are as lovely as snowflakes, perfect in their own design.

Ideally, jadeite and nephrite should be pure white. They almost never are. When found, pure white jade is above all price. The Chinese have a saying, "There are one hundred colors of white jade." Our English converse of this philosophy, "All cats look gray in the dark," is surely much less constructive and farther from the truth underlying all things.

Here is one of the great charms of jade, both nephrite and jadeite: their colors range from pure white to deepest black. Chloromelanite is always black of a depth not to be approached by the most witch-ridden midnight. The endless colors of jade are the result of each stone's individual experience in the earth. Admixture of other bases in the fundamental combination of minerals produces such colors as no other group of stones possesses. Green jadeite—known as jewel jade the world around —is beholden for its intense greenness to chromium, the coloring matter of emerald. Green nephrite owes its color to the presence in it of iron.

It is easy to see why green jade has so widely captured the fancy of the world, almost to the exclusion of the other colors. There are green jades, both jadeite and nephrite, which surpass all greenness on earth, except that of grass and bloom. But to my mind jades of other colors—of almost any other color you can mention—are equally beautiful. The Chinese invented thousands of phrases to describe these varying colors, names which often sound poetic just by themselves.

The toughness which gives it virtual immortality, the varying colors which give it mystery and enchantment, the feel of jade in the hand, indescribably cool and hard—these are some of the qualities which make it, physically, among the most interesting of stones.

I have so far not mentioned its mystic meanings for the Chinese, its great and noble and exciting history everywhere. It will be necessary to do this briefly to touch off the dreams and studies of those who would like to go farther afield. But even without its great world history and the burden of sentiment and good luck which it bears, jade is a noble stone here and now, one of the great new mineral finds of this continent.

I say it is a great new find, and by that, I do not mean that it is comparable with uncovering the Kohinoor diamond with the toe of a casual boot nor that it has any commercial value equal to that of gold or silver, uranium or oil, or even tin. Its commercial value is distinctly limited and always has been, even in China. But jade has now, as it has always had, the power to enchant its finders, to supply them with adventure and satisfaction and romance. Find it, cut it, polish it—and you are a stout Cortez, standing silent upon a peak in Darien, although I believe the historians have pointed out that it was not Cortez at all. Finding jade on this continent—to anyone who loves stones—is like discovering ten thousand acres of unexplored frontier, wilderness where no man has trod.

I have said that jade got its name on this continent, and so it did, but by as curious a series of mishaps and misunderstandings as anyone could imagine. The earliest name of jade was the Chinese pictograph *yu*, designated by a string of beads. Centuries after its classical glory in the Orient, the Spanish explorers in Central America found our early Indians using amulets of the hard mysterious stone, firm in the faith that they would cure kidney diseases and other quite earthly ailments. The explorers called these amulets *piedra de ijada*. The French who followed them wrote it *pedre de l'ejade*. A happy-go-lucky English printer decided to omit the Gallic apostrophe and called it *le jade*. Jade it has remained.

3

Symbolism in Jade

EVERYWHERE from the beginning of time mystery has enveloped the origins of this stone. Although the Chinese have revered it and used it widely for centuries, the original sources of jade in China itself are obscure.

Students of the great periods of Chinese carving know that native sources for jade were exhausted by A.D. 220, the end of the Han dynasty. The early jades of the Shang dynasty (from about 1766 B.C. to 1122 B.C.) and of Chou (from about 1122 B.C. to 256 B.C.) give us wonderful, if incomplete, glimpses of the people who lived at that time and of the high development of their art. But they tell us nothing at all about the origin of the jade itself.

From about the dawn of the Christian era, Turkestan became the chief source of jade for China. Jade was discovered in Burma at a much later date—about the thirteenth century. The jades of Turkestan are largely nephrite; those from Burma —especially the emerald or jewel jades—are jadeite. The original earliest jades of China were nephrite.

But though we know certainly that jade has a history among men from Neolithic—if not Mesolithic—times, we do not know where the Chinese first found it awash in their streams or first mined it from the earth. We do not know what artisan first had the courage to carve it into an ax—for one of the most fascinating things about working with jade is that it is virtually impossible to work with it at all. The toughness which makes it so enduring and so valuable defies any instrument except the finest abrasive and the most diligent application of time. It has always done so. Yet what was the Stone Age for western man was quite likely the jade age of China. When primitive man in the Orient first fashioned tools for his protection and use, he made them of jade, at what cost in time and effort no one can know who has not worked with jade. Jade adzes, axes, and other early tools of China are no less a tribute to twilight man's patience than to his intelligence. They are also a tribute, perhaps, to his stubbornness.

But antiquity alone cannot explain the reverence in which the Chinese have always held jade. Nor can the physical character of jade alone explain it—though its physical character is sufficient fascination for anyone who loves stones; nor can its elusiveness in the earth, the mystery of its beginnings and its sources. It must surely be a combination of all these, plus such an accumulation of history and affection and high art as would swamp any simple stone which lacked the structural complexities of jade.

There is scarcely a compliment or a graceful phrase which can be turned in your direction among truly well-brought-up Chinese that does not somewhere compare your virtues—or your wife or your lotus garden or the last course of your dinner —to a perfect piece of jade. There is a phrase in that language most rich in figures of speech which describes total destruction: "Then let jade and stone alike be destroyed." Less imaginatively we say: "Let the good perish with the evil." Happily for the survival of civilization, some pieces of jade have always been salvaged from among the stone.

By its ancient Chinese name, yu, jade has been a part of the language of cultivated men since 2953 B.C., when Fu Hsi devised the important change from knotted cords to written signs as symbols of the spoken word. The word yu is impossible to translate into English. The word "jade" certainly does not do

[17]

it. One Chinese definition of that all-embracing word reads: "the stone possessing the cardinal virtues, pure, precious, valuable and beautiful." Another calls it "the mysterious, alluring, mystic stone." It is certainly all these. On every continent of the round globe it has proved itself mysterious and alluring.

Several centuries before Christ, a minister of state asked Confucius why jade of all stones was most highly to be prized by modern man. The great philosopher answered: "Like virtue, though faulty, it does not hide its good points; when superior, it does not conceal its defects." The ancient Chinese *Book of Rites* gives a partial answer to the hold of jade upon the imagination of man: "It is of warm, liquid and moist aspect like benevolence; it is solid, strong and firm like politeness; when struck, it gives out a pure far-reaching sound, vibrating long but stopping like music; like truth it gives out a bright rainbow; it shows a pure spirit among the hills and streams; and in the whole world there is no one that does not value it."

If this interpretation were valuable for nothing else, it would be worth while for its picture of truth as giving out a bright rainbow. Less thoughtful people have assumed that truth gives off a single white blinding light, and not knowing so well what to look for, have often missed it.

Throughout Chinese literature and philosophy, jade is regarded as the most beautiful substance in which the thought of man can be embodied. Because it cannot be soiled and because ordinary—or even extraordinary—friction does not injure it, the ancients quite properly considered it a symbol of the inviolate reason of man.

The Chinese have never known for sure where their jade came from originally. But fancifully they have given it a mystic and delightful origin. According to a legend of the twelfth century B.C., a distinguished statesman, Lou Shune, disguised as a poor fisherman, went to the holy brook, Wei Soi, to meditate and commune with the holy order above. Philosopherlike, he fished as he communed. In the stream he caught a carp in which he found a tablet of pure jade. It was inscribed with a message from the sacred order that the next dynasty of the kingdom would be known as Chou, that it was to be the golden age of China, and that Lou Shune must assist with its coming.

Thus it came to pass; and Lou Shune, who had been despised for many years by political leaders because of his Taoist philosophy, became Chancellor of China. Then followed that gentle time when the people of China were ruled ably and justly by the same great dynasty for almost 900 years—all because of the blessing bestowed by Lou Shune's jade tablet.

There have been historians snide enough to suggest that what we now look upon as the golden age of China may have had its brass as well; that with its jade was considerable stone; and that all was not harmony, sweetness, and light in that ancient time. But even the spoilsports agree that it was a very remarkable time indeed; and since it was all so very long ago and so little remains of the actual record, no one can actually deny the benign influence of the tablet of jade.

Still another story—whether part fact or all fancy we scarcely know—recounts the discovery of jade in China in the seventh century before Christ. Ben Wo, a mineralogist, it is said, crossing the Gin San Mountains, saw a giant carved phoenix of pure jade jutting from a peak. After he had carried it carefully to the king, the savants refused to believe that this was truly jade and that it was truly an outcropping of the native hill. Banishment and heaven only knows what torment were the lot of Ben Wo. But he was justified after all, many years later, when a new king ordered the jade phoenix cut in two that its worth might be appraised. It proved to be of such astonishing beauty that part of it was made into the royal seal. A good many years too late to be of much comfort to his aching bones, Ben Wo was given the title of "Grand Master of Optimism." Faith in his jade had undoubtedly kept an enduring spirit from curdling. The royal seat of jade made from Ben Wo's phoenix, passing along to the king, Shu Wang, was regarded as of such worth that an offer of fifteen cities in exchange for it was refused.

The earliest carved jades known to us date from the Shang dynasty. From the priceless records that remain to us of that distant time, it is certain that the carving of jade had reached a high degree of development by the twelfth to fourteenth centuries before Christ. The eloquent carved jade pieces of the Chou dynasty, which immediately followed the Shang, are tomb pieces, possessing religious significance. Generally, these are the *pi*, flat circular disks, representing heaven; and *kuei*, flat oblong rectangular tablets, representing the east quarter. Our actual knowledge of the way men lived and thought at this ancient time is sketchy in the extreme. But those jade votive pieces tell us the most that we shall ever know about their religion and ceremonies.

One cannot go back far enough in Chinese history to find a time when jade was not looked upon as almost divine material, the symbol of priestly and kingly power. Today the symbol of the Chinese Republic is a seal of jade, and the highest order of the Republic is the *Order of Brilliant Jade*.

In the religion of the Chou dynasty, jade pieces represented heaven, earth and the four quarters. Heaven was represented by blue jade, *pi*; earth by yellow jade, *tsking*; the east quarter by green jade, *kuei*; the south by jade tinted red, *chang*; the west by white jade, *hu*; the north by black jade, *huang*. There was room in the spectrum of jade colors to represent the whole universe.

By the Chinese jade was classified into three general groups: *Ke yu*, ancient jade passed on from one generation to another; *Chin yu*, old jade dug from the earth; and *Han yu*, jade buried with the dead.

The classic nine colors of nephrite jade during the great ages of carving were: translucent white, indigo blue, moss green, plume-of-the-kingfisher, yellow, cinnabar red, blood red, lacquer black, and opaque white. (The last, called sra, was and is the most highly prized of all jade colors.)

But these were by no means all the colors of jade. There were—and are—thousands. But surely only the Chinese would have had the imagination and affection to call the colors of jade by such names as: sunflower, cassia, chrysanthemum, rose madder, apple, melon peel, date skin, sandalwood, moss, fruit flesh, and spinach. There were and are: chicken bone, duck bone, antelope, leopard, fish belly, nightingale, cow hair, water, morning dew, sky-after-the-rain, frozen-slush-veined-with-clouds. There were: candle red, rouge-of-the-cosmetics, red-of-a-child's-face, wine, purple-of-the-veins, porcelain, silk, and paint black. In addition to multicolored jades, the Chinese also speak of fragrant jades, but these are probably jades buried so long with the spices and perfumes of the grave that they have taken on a fragrance.

As you will discover if you attempt even to cut and polish it, much less carve it, jade presents a great challenge to the lapidary. One of the marvels of the world is how the great artists of the golden age of jade carving could have achieved the incredible beauty and fragility of jade objects, a beauty never matched or approached since. All this fabulous work was done apparently by means of thongs and abrasive stick drawn back and forth through fine diamond, sapphire, and ruby dust, with endless patience and artistry. A great many of the pieces so carved have the delicacy and thinness of flower petals.

It is said by A. Livingston Gump, who owns an extremely fine collection of jade, that only the Chinese possess the jade madness to work properly with jade. He may be right. To illustrate his point, he cites the history of the Emperor Ch'ien Lung, who reigned between 1736 and 1796. It was his pleasure to order the execution of the impossible by his jade workers. Once he ordered—and received—a piece of translucent emerald jade, measuring just 2 by 1 1/2 inches, carved thin as parchment, with lace on one side designed in peonies, butterflies, and birds, and on the other a scroll representing the Buddhist unending knot of happiness. Compared with this task, inscribing the Lord's Prayer on the head of a pin is work for a sculptor.

Properly enough during the hundreds of years when jade carving was at its height, the jade workers of China enjoyed unusual privileges. They were allowed to work when and as the spirit moved, so that their work should ever be a labor of love, not of necessity. Many a fine carved piece undoubtedly required years in the working. But it is probably an exaggeration to suppose, as has sometimes been stated, that a lifetime was often devoted to carving a single piece. For workers so manifestly skillful, years would have sufficed. But unlike us today, they were unafraid of time and considered any amount of it well spent perfecting a single vessel for the royal tea. How right they were any fine museum housing a specimen of carved jade will testify.

The jade carvers of ancient China belonged to several great periods, and artists of each period used their own distinctive designs and ornamentation. Though we know surely that artisans were working skillfully in jade from the eighteenth century before Christ, there is a still earlier period—the Hsia, according to legend—in which jade carving was a high art. The bird design appears to have been favored. Our museums boast some very fine examples of the carved jades of the Shang dynasty. These frequently feature the worm motif—but such glorified worms, certainly transfiguring all creatures of common dust! The great early Chou pieces are uniformly and rigidly classical, carved in royal and priestly characters. Scholars are generally agreed that the carving of jade reached its greatest artistic development between the third and fifth centuries. Work in jade has, since that time, occasionally equaled the beauty of those pieces, but never surpassed them.

The world-wide reputation of jade as the good-luck stone is so ancient that no one can say when it first achieved that happy designation. The famous green jade *ji*, once the scepter of a

Chinese statesman, is called "the stone as you wish it." To a degree, any owner of a fine jade piece takes a certain comfort to his soul in the mere possession of a stone so well thought of by so many men. Long before the stone received its unromantic cognomen "jade," the Chinese believed it to provide a general sort of health insurance. Finely powdered jade was frequently served to royal personages in one liquid or another, as a tonic, or perhaps for the same reason that prompted Cleopatra to swallow pearls in a wine bowl—assuming that we know the reasons prompting that captious female.

There is a very ancient superstition that good luck overtakes those particularly who wear jade on Fridays. Though less lofty souls than Confucius have endowed jade with superstitions relating to material blessings, the philosopher himself seems to have believed that its chief value was to remind man of the integrity of his mind and the incorruptibility of his soul. That is enough of a mission for a stone of such great intrinsic beauty.

Mysterious, alluring, and mystic, jade has been through more than five thousand years of the history of mankind. Up to our own time, jade had been found in place in upper Burma, where large quarries were discovered in the thirteenth century; in central India; and in Siberia among glacial deposits. Through the centuries there have been announcements of true jade in place in various quarters of central Europe and in New Zealand.

About two decades ago a report was made of the finding of a large number of jade boulders in Alaska, 150 miles north of the Kowak River. Some also were reported along the lower Fraser and upper Lewes Rivers in British Columbia. But these reports caused very little stir anywhere. For the most part, they were scarcely credited; and no one was sufficiently moved to do very much about them.

Then something happened. Perhaps jade madness began to stir a little in our blood. Perhaps the thought of uncovering in the New World a wealth of the world's oldest jewel stone began to appeal to our frontier spirit. But those of us who cared saw a few oddly assorted clues, made a few lucky finds, did some putting of two and two together, went prospecting, went inquiring into other people's business—and lo and behold! Where a generation ago any sober man of science would have assured you there was no jade whatsoever in America, now you will find even the most conservative agreeing that jade is truly here—in what volume we do not yet know, in what range of quality we cannot guess.

What the clues are and what the finds have been and how much adventure lies along the paths of jade in America are the subject of the chapters that follow. I have been an unconscionably long time getting to it. But this happens to be the kind of mystery that begins in a far-off continent, in a time when all the world was new. I hope it is also the kind that will have no end, like the search for truth, of which jade is a symbol. And in the meantime, as a great philosopher once said of truth itself, the search for it is perhaps even more desirable than finding it.

4

Clues to the Mystery

MY ADVENTURES with jade in America began in 1920. I remember very well the day—an exceptionally hot summer day—when a large box from Alaska was plumped down on my office desk. In case it seems curious that one whose business is cheese should regularly have had such oddly assorted items as Indian artifacts and stuffed birds and almost any other object in the world except cheese put on his desk during business hours, let me say that I learned long ago that a man cannot do his best work in any sort of commerce unless he is able, at any moment, to turn his mind away from his business and its problems completely. He should also be able to take a short nap in his chair. This will keep him from being half asleep the remainder of the day.

And if he has even an indifferently good collection of small stones on top of his desk, he will never be tempted into those idle and profitless habits of doodling with which so many people waste their time and their talent. This habit of mine—keeping boxes of strange things coming to me from all parts of the world—has always been a matter of interest and curiosity to my secretary and to the boys in the mailing department. They have never known whether a package would contain gems or junk. I have never known either—and that is what has always sent me enthusiastically into mountains of daily mail.

On this particular day, I was busy making plaster of Paris

impressions of the figurines on some early Oriental seals, and I had just been working on one carved in extremely fine green jade. But fascinating as the seals were, I laid them aside to examine the contents of the Alaskan box. What I found inside was so exciting that I put the seals by gladly, for though I am proud of the hundreds of seals which I own, I had found a hobby of much more absorbing interest for me. Within the box I saw at once a deep green stone, reminiscent in color at least of the carved seal.

A letter accompanying the box said that the green rock was jade—and, indeed, it was vaguely kidney shaped and might almost have been the very piece which caused the Spaniards to give the material its name. My bushwhacker friend said that this jade had been acquired, while on a timber-cruising trip, from the Haidan Indians on Queen Charlotte Islands off the coast of British Columbia. He had no notion where they got it.

The stone, though uncut, was grooved after the fashion of our Alaskan Indians, in so far as we have been able to reconstruct their methods. Apparently it was their practice to sit on a sandy beach (where a mixture of sand and water was readily at hand for an abrasive) and patiently draw buckskin thongs across the stone to carve out primitive cutting tools. The ten-pound kidney-shaped piece of jade varied in color from light to very dark green, with brownish-yellow streaks running through it. It was nephrite jade unmistakably, as I discovered after I had it tested.

This sizable chunk of uncut jade, the largest I had ever seen up to that time—for I had really seen only the ancient Chinese carved pieces—was fascinating just in itself. Its mingled colors, its immediately apparent hardness, the primitive workmanship left unfinished—these would have interested the most casual observer, I think. For that piece of jade—long since made into pins and good-luck pieces and rings in my workshop—was a noble thing in itself.

I admired this treasure so much that I wrote my friend asking that he send all the jade he could come by. Piece by piece and chunk by chunk, I acquired about ninety pounds of this really beautiful jade from Alaska, its source unknown. Some of the pieces had been carved into axes, chisels, and other cutting tools; some were entirely untouched by abrasive. Then I began the most intensive reading—and correspondence with everyone on earth I could think of who might have a clue to the mystery—to discover the source of this Alaskan jade.

Pooh! was the consensus, though couched in gentler terms in the main. "That's easy—it came from Asia, across the Bering Strait!" A logical enough conclusion, I suppose! But I couldn't help thinking that if my ninety-odd pounds of uncut jade were any sample—and the stuff is very heavy and unwieldy—then the Asiatics had a mighty tough pull of it across that Bering Strait, assuming that they brought anything else with them.

The popularly accepted theory concerning the source of jade which has been found in chunk and carved form in many places on this continent was well summed up by Dr. George Frederick Kunz in his book *The Curious Lore of Precious Stones*, first published in 1913. Dr. Kunz said at that time:

The source of the prehistoric jade (nephrite and jadeite) found in Europe, and also of that worked into ornaments by the Indians before the Spanish Conquest of America, was long the subject of contention among mineralogists and archaeologists. In Germany this question was denominated the nephritfrage, and the most notable contribution to the discussion was the great scientific and scholarly work issued by Heinrich Fischer. His conclusion was that as there was no evidence of the existence of these minerals outside of a few localities in Asia, the European and American supply must have been brought to these parts of the world from Asia, and that hence the presence of these jade artifacts in America clearly pointed to commercial intercourse at an early period between the American continent and Asia, and might be regarded as offering a strong argument in favor of an Asiatic origin for an American civilization. According to this theory the prehistoric jade objects found in Europe must have had a similar source, and would constitute a proof of the existence of traffic with remote points in Asia at a date long previous to that commonly accepted.*

I would be the last person to quarrel with the theory of widespread early commerce between Asia and America—and it seems to me an Asiatic origin for early American civilization is borne out by many facts—but not by the presence of jade artifacts on the continent. Why, I asked myself, despite that grandiose series of high jinks known as the *nephritfrage*, wouldn't it be equally logical that Orientals who knew how to work in jade had found jade on this continent—and had thus used it as well as they knew how? Since even the original sources of jade in Asia itself were obscure, why should they not be equally obscure all over the world?

Since jade pieces, carved with varying degrees of art and skill, were left by every one of our great early civilizations in both North and South America, it seemed to me much more logical that the people who first came here, from whatever continent, found their raw materials nearer at hand than distant Asia.

Mexico, Yucatan, and Peru had proved a rich treasure house of prehistoric American jade pieces, many of which are carved intricately. From various signs the archaeologists had concluded that the Aztecs valued first jade, then turquoise, then gold, as materials for jewel and votive pieces. The grim sacred well of Chichen Itzá yielded up many exquisite jade pieces to bear out the belief that the Mayas too held jade in the very highest esteem.

As a matter of fact, the very earliest dated art object of America is the jade Tuxtla statuette, a work of art of the Mayan Indians. From the glyphs carved into the statuette, it is dated 96 B.C. (by correlation of the Mayan and Christian chronolo-

---

* From *The Curious Lore of Precious Stones* by George Frederick Kunz. Copyright, 1913, 1941, by Mrs. Ruby Kunz Zinsser, published by J. B. Lippincott Company.

gies). Thus a finished jade work of art in America antedates Columbus' discovery of this continent by about sixteen hundred years. Earlier classified as nephrite, the Tuxtla statuette is now classified as jadeite. Plowed up in 1902 in the district of San Andres de Tuxtla on the gulf coast of Mexico, this earliest dated treasure of American art is the property of the United States National Museum.

So there was jade in Alaska and jade which had been familiarly, almost carelessly used for many centuries by the Haidas; there was jade painstakingly carved into ceremonial pieces by the Aztecs and Mayas; there was jade (though these finds were rare) in the flesh knives and an occasional arrowhead of our Far Western American Indians. Though the Spanish were but Johnnies-come-lately to this continent when they gave jade its name, they found the stone here in its carved form in great plenty. Apparently it had been in familiar use by the artisans of the New World for centuries.

Where jade had been used so long—though certainly never so well as in China—it seemed to me jade must exist. Its sources on this continent, like so many mysterious chapters in the history of early man, might very easily have been lost. But if jade did exist here—as float in our streams or buried in our mountains—I determined to do at least a bit of stirring about to find it. Besides, I was personally in great need of more jade!

5

Jade in California

SINCE MY MEETING with a band of Oregon rock-hounds, I had become, if not the most skillful of the breed, certainly the most enthusiastic. One can set up a working lapidary shop with equipment either simple or elaborate, and have just as much fun either way. I started with a single diamond saw and a rather inadequate polishing machine. And I have since worked up to a somewhat extensive line of machines, some of which I have invented myself or adapted to my own use out of very curious machinery indeed. I can now stand with a piece of rough jade in my hand at one end of my workshop, cut and slice it, get a piece down to jewel size and shape, carry it through all the various stages of polishing, mount it, and put it aside to be shared with someone tomorrow—all in a series of steps as direct as an automobile assembly line.

But I do not have any more fun than I had with my first diamond saw and polishing machine, which enabled me for the first time to get inside a stone—and see what lay within! I don't have any less fun now, either. In the case of a great many stones, cutting and polishing is a highly exciting experience. In the case of jade, the process opens up a whole new world. For jade in the rough looks like nothing much at all. Generally heavily encased in a crust of most unpromising tough material, it has little color. If you passed by a piece of it and kicked it aside as worthless, I shouldn't much blame you. But you might break your toe; and you would be missing one of the greatest possible thrills.

For you never know what may lie within a piece of jade—what colors, what patterns, what shimmer of beauty. Of course, as you work in about any piece of jade, you will find much material that is not of gem quality, much that undercuts, much that is dark-specked. Jade is not all pure gem jade any more than a saint is all saint and no sinner.

I had worked in my basement lapidary shop a long time before I had the courage or temerity to cut into that original ten-pound Alaskan piece. (That piece, by the way, had been water-polished and sand-ground, so that its beauty was at once apparent when I received it.) Cutting into it, making gem stones from it was so exciting—the results so amazingly beautiful—that I stayed up more than half of many a night working with it. I could get up hardly early enough in the morning to share some special jade gem with someone!

Since my jade had to be shared—and I wanted to share it as far and wide as I could—I conceived the idea of setting up a jade merit award for my fellow workers at the company. Jade rings were presently awarded to men and women in the company who had given outstanding service in one department or another. After a number of years that original ten-pound chunk and all the ninety pounds of Alaskan jade which I had acquired —except, of course, Indian-finished artifacts which I had kept intact—were about gone. I was almost scraping the bottom of the barrel. I did not particularly want—even if I could have gotten—jade from Burma or Turkestan. I wanted jade from America and, as I thought even then, of America!

I had made one tentative effort to secure jade from another source which had been hinted but not verified: New Zealand. But what I received was New Zealand greenstone, a quite jade-like stone. Even for greenstone, however, the sample I received was not of gem quality. Subsequently I have received true jade from New Zealand, and at its best I think it may surpass in beauty jade from any other source. Someone, knowing my need, sent a specimen of what purported to be South African jade, but it was not of gem quality either. In fact, it wasn't jade at all!

At the time when I thought I should have to give up working with jade—and awarding it for merit—a mineral dealer in Oregon, in a small advertisement in one of the lapidary magazines, offered for sale a few slices of what he called American jade, at seventy-five cents the slice. Though my hopes were not particularly high, I ordered a few slices of this material.

When the box arrived, I was excited, for the pieces I examined had many of the characteristics of Chinese jade, not quite so hard or tough perhaps, but beautifully mottled green and white of the precise color of Chinese spinach jade.

Without having a careful analysis made, I could not be sure that this was nephrite jade, but I worked with it anyway and found it extremely satisfying and beautiful. As I had suspected they might be, these green slices of stone sent by the Oregon dealer were the mineral called vesuvianite or californite—a jade impostor sometimes listed as entitled to bear the name of jade. But its intrinsic beauty was so great—and my hope was so high that true nephrite jade might be found near the source of the californite—that I had to find out more about it.

I wrote at once to the Oregon dealer who had offered the material for sale. He said that he had bought it from an Indian who had driven by in an old Ford car bearing a California license plate. He assumed that the Indian must have driven into Oregon from that state, but that he couldn't have had a long journey back, for the car obviously wouldn't take him far. This was all the information he had. The name, the tribe, the home of the californite-bearing Indian were a complete mystery.

But jade has been traced through a greater maze of uncertainty than was posed by the California Indian.

In solving this particular riddle, I was very lucky to know an ex-prospector and miner who considered tracking down an unknown purveyor of jade a very routine assignment. With an outward show of the greatest indifference, even boredom, he told me he would go on this peculiar search just the way the owner of a lost donkey would do: by asking himself where he would go if he were a donkey. He was in nowise daunted when I told him not to come back until he had discovered the source of the green californite. It is impossible to intimidate your true prospector by telling him not to come back until he has succeeded. Coming back to his point of departure is generally the last thing he wants to do anyway.

But for all his elaborate casualness, this prospector was a true rockhound. Only a man of that special nose for gems would have undertaken it. He was a better sleuth than I, or even he, knew. He was a few weeks on the way, but he proceeded simply by taking the shortest route to California from the gem dealer's shop. The trail took him across the border of Oregon to a wild and beautiful part of northern California. Though he had taken the shortest route, he spent enough time along the way to talk to everybody and question everybody, red and white.

In the vicinity of a village which rejoices in the name of Happy Camp, he talked with many natives who had heard tell of pretty green stones being found near by. Not much was thought of the stones, although a number of old-timers had thought a good deal of them. By lingering, following up many hints and fairy-tale directions, going off on wild tangents, and by various methods all his own, my prospector friend finally found what he had come for. Walking one day on a lonely mountainside about six miles from Happy Camp, he came upon great boulders of stone, their deep green color only glimpsed through a heavy coating of brownish-green. They were found mostly near a roaring mountain stream where plenty of trout could be had for the taking. I think he must have stopped to do some fishing. At least he took plenty of time about announcing his discovery, sending me word casually on a penny post card instead of phoning or wiring. As soon as the word came, I made utmost haste to buy the entire mountain area—californite, trout, roaring water, and all. I hoped that near the californite we would find true jade! If we found nothing more than the californite, it would be treasure enough for a lapidary and beauty enough to keep me busy a lifetime. So I bought it—and since the site had long since been abandoned as an important source for gold, I got the claim for a small price.

Then a strange thing came to light: the Indian and I had been by no means the first to think that this California mountain held jade. When we came to record the transfer, I found that the property had been known originally as the Chan Jade Claim. Apparently one who should have known (a Chinese to whom jade is sacred) thought he had discovered a mountain of pure jade.

The luckless Chan—whose story is as grim as any penny dreadful of the Far West—was more nearly right than he lived to know. Though much of Chan's mountain has thus far proved to be californite of gem quality, a substantial volume of pure nephrite jade has come to light. And we are still prospecting. This mountain of jade—and other jewel stones—stands some 4,000 feet above the north fork of Indian Creek. Jagged peaks of californite and jagged peaks of jade—boulders of all sizes and shapes, some true jade, some californite—are richly and bountifully present. Not all the jade and jadelike material of Chan jade mountain is the green color so familiarly known. Resting at the bottom of the creek is a white boulder wonderful beyond description. Estimated to weigh about eighty tons —for I have never had it removed—it almost has the color of the foaming water. I have worked with small chunks taken from this boulder—and it has been authoritatively classified as nephrite jade.

Jade in California

An eighty-ton piece of white jade and trainloads of californite of rich green are not the only glories of this mountain. There is a translucent varicolored green serpentine (very frequently found near jade) which, when it is sliced thin and polished finely, resembles that Chinese jade color, sky-after-the-rain. There is californite of mottled pink and black; there is jade almost true black—black almost of the intensity of chloromelanite. There are jades whose greenness is subdued to brown that resembles the color of ancient Chinese tomb jade.

On my first prospecting trip to this kingdom, I could scarcely believe the extent of the wonders lying ready to be cut and polished and worn and loved. The material appears in the form of boulders, varying in size from small pebbles to many tons. To get material from the mountain, we have broken up some of the larger formations either by blasting or with a sledge. Blasting always ruins a lot of good material; the sledge is best, but it is tough work. After the blasting or sledging, pieces of suitable size for a diamond saw are selected. By wetting each piece of stone thoroughly, you can see the true colors as they will appear when they are carefully polished.

Only after the pieces have been sawed into slabs from one-eighth to one-half inch in thickness can you tell whether the particular piece will produce suitable gems. In many of the specimens which I have taken in a packsack from that mountain, I have found spots of pure free yellow gold. Let me say, in case this circumstance should precipitate another gold rush, that the cost of extracting this small amount of free gold far exceeds its value. Spots of yellow gold, however, do add an interesting color to many of the gem pieces.

Just how much of the Chan Jade Claim of California will prove to be nephrite jade I do not know—nor care. It has been established that some of the material is true jade in float. That much jade in place lies beneath the crust I haven't the least doubt. One day the vein beneath will be found. When the time comes I hope to be on hand with pickax ready.

But though I count myself, after a fashion, the discoverer of this particular jade find in California, taking pride for it is really ridiculous: it had been known as the Chan Jade Claim for almost a century before I heard of it. No one—following the ill-fated Chan—ever paid any attention. But Chan knew—and died with his secret.

Chan was a man of mystery even during his brief and merry lifetime. Apparently he first sailed through the Golden Gate in search of fortune and adventure in the early fifties. "Mystery Wong" he was called along the Barbary coast, if the word of Happy Camp's most faithful historian has it right. At any rate, Wong Chan traveled from San Francisco to Indian Town to grab his share of a mine from which more than a million dollars in gold was uncovered in a matter of days. Indian Town was near Happy Camp, and Chan combed the creeks about the area for further riches, presumably gold. On one of his sorties he found a sprinkling of jade boulders in Indian Creek. Knowing that in his own land jade was in great demand—and apparently recognizing it when he saw it—Chan looked further for the source of the mysterious green stone. On the bank of the south fork, he caught sight of a series of giant green boulders—boulders of jade, or so Chan believed.

The legend of Happy Camp has it that Chan was so jubilant over his find, which to him meant far more than gold, that he decided to celebrate his discovery. After posting his claim his first act was to build a large cabin suitable for a celebration in the grand manner. To this day residents of Happy Camp recall their fathers' telling of the commotion occasioned in transporting large barrels of whisky and other refreshments up the mountainside.

The guests, who had no interest whatsoever in the jade or were not even advised of its presence, proved to be considerably interested in the refreshments. After several days of imbibing, the fighting and the bloodletting began. A wild flight ensued from the scene of this festivity, and guests returned to their more sober existences by the most rapid of all courses.

Poor Chan—his party a failure, his jade all unmined, his gold quite useless—was either shot and killed or fell over a hazardous bit of his own jade-filled terrain and broke his neck. No one knows—or no one has ever told. The inevitable skull found in Dead Man's Gulch was reported to be Chan's.

On the stroke of midnight in late summer every year, the eerie sound of the fiddles of Chan's party can be heard, and the wraith of Wong Chan with his long black queue can be seen dancing along the trail from Chan jade mine to Dead Man's Gulch. Either I have never been on the mountaintop on the right night of summer, or Chan's ghost is at peace. But I find his a sad story indeed. Here was a man who, in the early fifties, could have told the world that jade does exist in America, could have luxuriated in a mountain filled with jewels sacred to his race. Poor Chan. I hope he enjoyed his party while it lasted!

6

Jade in Alaska

WITH NEPHRITE from my California mountain coming to me regularly, I had an American jade source equal to my special need of jade, though no vast wealth of it. The true nephrite had to be carefully selected from the mass of other jadelike material; and since I have never attempted to make the somewhat elaborate determinations for jade in my own shop—the hardness, specific gravity, and other lapidary tests—I had to have this work done outside. Concern over whether the material from my claim in California were nephrite or californite never kept me from working with whatever I found beautiful.

But naturally, a jade award is an award of jade and can be made from no other stone. So everything that went into jade rings had to be nephrite—and of good clear green. The jade award finally became so popular among the ten thousand people eligible for one that more jade rings were needed than there were hours in the day and night to make them. So regretfully I finally had to turn over some of the actual cutting, polishing, and mounting of the jade to outside lapidaries and jewelers. Had I not done so, I should never have had time to pursue further explorations and discoveries in jade itself.

Those adventures—from the time of the finds in California—followed upon one another so fast that I cannot recount them chronologically, but must do so as they come to mind, one find crowding another and some of them overlapping in point of time. You know how it is when you first encounter a strange word in your native tongue. You have never seen it before in print—and all at once you see it everywhere: on the front page of every newspaper, in every magazine article that strikes your eye. The word was there all the time; it was only revealed to you when the bottom dropped out of your abysmal ignorance. To a degree, it was so with jade finds in America. For centuries jade did not exist here in its natural state at all. Then between the middle nineteen-thirties and the middle forties, it began cropping up everywhere—or rumors that it had cropped up flourished as the green bay tree.

My search for jade on this continent involved trying to track down the elusive stone in Alaska. Naturally, since the first American jade pieces I had ever held in my hand were those artifacts of the Queen Charlotte Islands off British Columbia, I was most persistent in my investigation of that territory. Though an occasional article on jade—and even an encyclopedia or two—mentioned briefly the finding of some jade boulders in the upper Fraser River, there the information ended. Who found jade in the upper Fraser no one seemed to know or care. Where he found it no one indicated. Whether any attempts were being made to find it again seemed to interest mineralogists less than practically any riddle on earth. If the Eskimos and Indians knew of jade in the north country, they weren't talking—or no one would listen, I couldn't be sure which!

I teased myself with the riddle. But that was as far as I got until 1933, when I found the first honest clue about Alaskan jade at that amazing spectacle and conglomeration of bedazzlement and bedizenment: the Century of Progress. Along with the side shows and the peep shows, the cotton candy and the red pop, there was many a sight really worth seeing. Among these was the Alaskan building.

And more impressive than the building or anything else in it was one Slim Williams who had charge of it. A more unlikely barker of circus wares was never seen than Slim. Long, lean, and bowed to about a thirty-degree angle, Slim looked as if he were made of nine parts tundra and one part iceberg. As a publicity stunt, Slim had driven a team of ten huskies all the way from Nome to Chicago. But that it was done in the name of publicity in no way detracted from the honestness and earnestness of the job Slim had done along the way. Anyone who doubts it is invited to drive a team of ten large dogs down just a mile and a half of State Street sometime.

At any rate, Slim, as far as I was concerned, was worth all the rest of the fair put together. The tundra and iceberg of his exterior surfaces concealed pure gold and asbestos—and I wouldn't wonder, uranium, down underneath—like many another unlikely-looking bit of Alaskan scenery. Slim fell into the way of coming up to the house for dinner when he couldn't stand the smell of hot dogs any longer. I have never had a more entertaining guest nor one who knew more about things close to mountains and rivers and streams and stones.

One evening as we sat chatting over some Indian arrowheads, seals, and the like, I noticed Slim's eyes wandering over the window ledge where I kept what was left of my green jade rocks from British Columbia. Finally he unwound himself from his chair, walked over, and, picking up one of the stones, said laconically, "What you doing with this stuff?"

"Why, Slim," I said, "that's jade!"

"You don't say!" he replied. "I know where there is a mountain of this stuff!"

"Where?" I asked.

"In northern Alaska."

I fixed him firmly with my eye. "Slim," I said, "you must be wrong. I've been trying to find someone up there who could tell me the source of this stuff for more than a year. So far, I haven't had a nibble!"

"There's plenty could tell you if they wanted to," said Slim. "If you've got a map, I'll show you just exactly where it is."

The only map of Alaska in my library was an old outmoded Canadian school geography which I had kept for sentimental reasons from boyhood days. There hasn't been much use trying to keep a map up to date since the year 1900 anyway. Slim turned to the old-fashioned map of Alaska, studied it carefully a moment, then pointed to a spot and said without any surprise whatsoever, "There you are. It's marked right here on this map—Jade Mountain!" Seeing that name in my ancient geography gave me something the feeling an explorer must have who goes to a spot which he considers wilderness only to find a sign reading, "Ringling Brothers Circus coming April 8th."

For sure enough, there it was—Jade Mountain—on the map. Later maps, more accurate maps, do not show such a name. Why that early Canadian map showed it I do not know.

Here, at last, was something tangible to work on: a map name, whether fanciful or real, and a man who had with his own eyes seen Jade Mountain. The way Slim described the place didn't encourage me to start right off for it. It was far removed from all civilization, he said, and a place didn't have to have hot and cold running water to be considered civilization by Slim. It was a good fifteen-day trip in by dog sled to the place of the shining green boulders, he said, where not even a right-minded Eskimo would travel if he could avoid it. Slim narrowed his eyes to slits, lifted my chunks of jade, and said that the load of provisions required for men and dogs for such a trip would be so great that a dog sled would be able to bring out only fifty pounds of rock at one time.

Polite as he was about my jade, Slim flatly refused to have anything to do with a jaunt so harebrained as a trip to Jade Mountain for a few green rocks. He said there might be some men still left in Alaska fool enough to undertake it—for he guessed there were those that would do anything for money.

But as for him, he would ask to be excused. He had already done one fool thing, bringing those good dogs down to a hot city. And that was enough to last a man another few years till the spirit was on him to do something else idiotic.

So Slim went off, leaving me with an important piece of the puzzle in my hands—and no hope of putting it into its proper place. He wrote me a few times after that and told me he guessed prospectors up his way had more sense than he'd given them credit for because he hadn't found anyone with little enough judgment to take a team of dogs to Jade Mountain.

By guile and the offer of money and the promise of high adventure, I tried every way I knew to get someone—anyone familiar with the Arctic Circle—to make the journey to that mountain of jade. Aviators are commonly very adventurous men and think no more of a fool's errand when it promises adventure than I do myself. But for some reason, whenever I mentioned jagged boulders of rock on a sheer incline, they urged me, almost in these very words, to go fly my own kite. One man flew over the spot in his plane, but on returning to Nome sent me the utterly disgusted message that I couldn't expect a flea to land in that spot without special landing gear.

I had about decided I'd have to learn to fly—or develop a flea's landing gear—if I was ever to discover anything more about the sources of Alaskan jade. But one Saturday morning years later, in November of 1944, I was going down the steps to my basement workshop to make some pins for friends of mine in Australia, when our doorbell was rung with extraordinary vigor. Outside was a stranger who matched in every way the vigor of his ring. On the balustrade of our front porch lay a tremendous chunk of beautiful light green material—shining in the sun and recognizable as true nephrite jade.

"My name is James Robbins, of the Arctic Circle Exploration Company," the man said. He could not have been more welcome if he had been Stanley and had just remarked, "Dr. Livingstone, I presume."

"I have just flown down from Kobuk, Alaska," he went on, "and I brought you a ninety-pound piece of Alaska jade."

I have never thought to ask Jim Robbins if he had had breakfast that morning. I hadn't—and I never even noticed it until long past lunch time. We went right on down to the basement—and we worked with that jade until one o'clock. Jim Robbins is one of the finest natural rockhounds I have ever known, for though his business is not strictly speaking jade—but gold and asbestos, and other readily marketable riches—he took as much joy in my cutting those first bright green pieces from his ninety-pound jade block as if he had been cutting them himself. A man cannot do fairer than that.

From that day to this, Jim Robbins has kept on sending me pieces of jade—boulders varying widely in both size and quality, some of exquisite gem jade, some indifferently fine, but all of them jade of the nephrite designation. These pieces, by special methods and daredeviltry all his own and by purchase from people equally oblivious to their own safety, have come mostly from the Jade Mountain area.

On many of his flights and visits beyond the Arctic Circle, Jim Robbins has picked up fascinating tales of jade in the old days in Alaska. The jade itself is proof that many of the tales—or others very like them—are certainly true.

As in the California finds, there was at least one other before me who discovered jade in this very spot—and valued what he found. Once again this "uncharted" jade country proved to have a river, tributary to the Kobuk, called the Shungnak. (The Eskimo word for the river, *Singok*, means "jade" in that language.) How the Eskimos must have laughed all these years while students solemnly asserted that all their jade had been borne across the Bering Strait. Eskimo-like, they enjoy their jokes just as much if nobody ever knows about them. And nobody ever did!

But back in 1906, a prospector was panning for gold on the Shungnak. He found a sizable chunk of jade in the river bed and, mentioning it as briefly as possible, gave up his search for gold and vanished with his jade. This secretive prospector—a German, possibly familiar with the old quarrel of the *nephritfrage*—took his jade to Germany where much of the early fine work in fashioning jade beads was done. A rumor got back to Alaska that his jade piece had been carved into a strand of beads of such beauty and luster that he had sold them for a king's ransom. I hope this is true, for I like to think that, unlike Chan of California, the Alaskan prospector managed to hang onto his jade long enough for it to bring him luck.

Jade Mountain is about forty miles from the joining of the Shungnak with the Kobuk. Those who have seen it—and I have not, for I have spent most of my time goading others into this remote spot—say that Jade Mountain looks like something done in water color by an artist for very young children. It must be coated with serpentine, for it is said to bear a glossy green color all over, like a jewel in itself. Serpentine, to geologists, is known as the mother of jade, and is frequently found with it. But beneath that crust of fibrous serpentine is jade of unestimated quantity and of worth unknown.

Jade Creek, which flows from the mountain, shows some jade in float. Some of it unfortunately is filled with black specks that undercut as you work it. Some of it is jewel jade. To find 10 per cent of jewel jade in a large piece is good finding, however. Jade is all like this—and when faulty, as Confucius had it, does not conceal its defect. In Jade Creek it is not unusual to find fifteen-ton boulders of pure nephrite jade.

Now that a few men have had the temerity to go to Jade Mountain, many men are trying it. Mining on a fairly extensive scale was done in the vicinity through the brief summer of 1945. But even so, the season of working is so short, the resistance of the material to being found in the first place and moved in the second is so great, that no one has any accurate guess as to what the total find may be. That it will prove enormous no one can doubt.

Jade in Alaska

Now that jade has been found in Alaska, we are uncovering a substantial Eskimoan mythology of jade and its sources, not so elaborate as Chinese mythology but suited well enough to our newer culture and more forthright Paul Bunyanism. The Eskimos of the far north beyond the Arctic Circle have a yarn to the effect that jade was first discovered in Alaska by a lovesick Indian youth.

He aspired, it seems, to the hand of the belle of the village. But as often happened, even in Indian times, the girl's mother saw in the youth only a pretentious and worthless nobody who would never amount to anything and would doubtless allow the family totem to go to wrack and ruin. She said a firm and positive "No"—and although those Indians would have appeared to live under matriarchy, her "No" proved to be the next to the last word.

The young man set himself a task worthy of Hercules. He said, "If I build your daughter a dwelling place all of jade, will I be worthy of her then?" Perhaps the mother also assumed that the family's store of jade axes and ornaments had been brought from Asia; for she readily assented to the bargain. The youth promptly set off for Jade Mountain—and returned with jade, too. Finally, he built a dwelling place all of shining green jade. Anyone knows the ending of this story in any language: he got the girl! According to the Eskimos to this day, the jade boulders found in the Kobuk River are the original doors and arches of that house.

Now that it has been proved that our early Alaskan Indians knew not only how to carve jade, but where to find it on this continent, the artifacts they made from this tough stone have taken on a new interest—at least for me. One of the Indian-fashioned jade artifacts which I acquired early from Alaska was a curious and tremendous spike, about twelve inches long.

It is flat, but nicely rounded at the edges; it tapers to a sharp point, having a large hole through its heavy upper end. It is rather obviously an instrument designed to kill, but is of such curious shape that I wondered long what particular creature it was intended to put out of the way. This weapon was found at the bottom of a shell bank on the shore of the Pacific near the Canadian border. It might have lain on the sandy floor with thousands of tons of shells heaped over it, except that the requirements of road building necessitated removing the shells. Near it were found the thoroughly bleached bones of a man.

I called upon a friend of mine who is a thoroughgoing scholar and likewise a man of considerable imagination, the perfect combination for a scientist if he is to make anything out of the truth when he finds it. I asked him, from his knowledge of such things, to reconstruct the story of the jade implement for me. After he had studied it a long time he said: "This instrument was fashioned, perhaps a thousand years ago, by a man who was undoubtedly a very ingenious inventor. He made it especially for taking one particular kind of meat— that of the walrus, one of the fiercest adversaries a man ever had. Through the hole in the head end of this instrument, he would have tied a buckskin thong. Then, it would have been his custom to wade into the sea as far as he dared, waiting nervelessly for hours until his prey came along. If used with sufficient skill, this jade piece would have done the job quickly and thoroughly. This time your friend's wits must have been wandering: the walrus got there first!"

This is only a small—and to me, strangely wistful—anecdote out of our lost and mysterious past. It tells no more, perhaps, of our civilization at that time than a bill of sale from a newspaper of 1861 tells about the causes of the Civil War. But it tells something. And the jade of our own continent, like that of ancient China, tells its story well—and will continue to tell it, I believe, with increasing clarity and eloquence, as we uncover more of our native jade at its source and as we divine its earliest uses here.

7

The Jade of Mexico

THE JADE IMAGES of Mexico and Central America, fascinating to historian and collector alike, are as far removed culturally as they are physically from the jade artifacts of Alaska. Both are nephrite jade, but the Alaskan pieces appear to have been carved mostly from rough stone, while those from Mexico are very largely carved from water-washed pebbles, smoothed by centuries of time before ever man laid thong and abrasive to the task.

If you examine the Mexican jade pebbles at the great museum in Mexico City, you will observe a remarkable thing: the faces carved upon them seem to be an international gallery. Some of the faces appear Oriental, some Norse, some Negroid. The artists who worked in this jade must surely have been world travelers.

But though they got their models abroad, I think they found the material with which they worked right at home. This is contrary to the generally accepted theory. But I think I can show—as nearly as such a thing may be—that if those early Mexicans had looked about them, they would have found just the material they were looking for on their home continent.

The workmanship of these artifacts is amazing. So far, no tool of sufficient hardness to cut this extremely tough stone has been found either in Mexico or Central America. The artists

[47]

must have worked with fine grit or sandstone moistened to adhere to an abrasive stick. To produce a likeness of face or figure with such equipment required a patience and skill which have long since gone out of the world.

The Aztecs, who loved and revered jade, did some very remarkable carving in it. So far, no Aztec piece has been found to rival the Chinese of the great ages. But they have a charm and a strangeness very suitable to the material. They also captured the individuality and character of the artists so long gone to dust, as do the Chinese pieces. Long after human bones have succumbed to the action of air-borne particles of quartz, the jade in which those fleshed bones worked endures. To me this wistful quality of varying mortality in all matter is one of the great fascinations of archaeology. And the all-but-deathless life of jade entitles it properly to the respect of peoples who venerate great age. The Aztecs were such people, as are the Chinese.

The riddle as to where the Aztecs and other Central American peoples acquired their jade is an ancient one. Water-washed pebbles of the exact type of the Mexican artifacts have been but rarely found anywhere else on earth, even in the Orient. But the scholars have been almost one in labeling Asia the source of our American artifacts.

I know a place where almost any day of the year the Mexicans and the Aztecs and the scholars could have found pebbles identical with those in which early Mexicans worked. And they can find them now, in great plenty, on the coast of our own California, right in the path, virtually, of thousands of American tourists each year.

This particular adventure began with a small box delivered to my desk one day, postmarked Monterey, California. I did not recognize the sender's name, but no matter—people are always sending me strange things. The contents of that box, however, did surprise me. Inside it were five or six small brilliantly polished jade pebbles. I knew the Mexican artifacts well, and aside from the fact that these were uncarved, it was plain that they were the same.

Since no one had even rashly suggested that pebbles similar to the wonderful Mexican ones might be found in the United States, I wrote at once to the sender of the packet. I tried to explain my interest carefully; I asked for as much information as the sender could give me about their source; and I asked for some more pebbles. My letter must have had too much of the hobbyist's enthusiasm in it, and not enough of the horse trader's reserve. I received no reply, no more pebbles. All was quiet around Monterey.

But it happened that I had a friend living thereabouts. And he looked up the sender of the jade pebbles for me. There never was a more unsatisfactory interview: the man would not be talked to; he would answer no questions; he refused to admit that he was, in fact, the sender.

Inquiry revealed that our self-contained explorer had been gathering these curios for some time, selling them for small sums to passers-by. But he had never led anyone to their source. I do not much blame him. It is not everyone who, finding a priceless treasure, takes joy in letting other men in on the secret. I gave him up. But I did not forget his mysterious pebbles.

Shortly afterward, through the greatest stroke of luck, another box of Monterey pebbles came to me from quite a different source. These were from an old friend, Will Ellington of Leland Stanford University. They were identical with the pebbles from the first box. And along with these arrived a letter telling the story of how Will came by them in the first place.

The story begins in 1880. In that year, a Californian was hunting sea lions up the Pacific coast near Monterey. At low tide, he chased his quarry into a cave. After he had made his kill, he discovered that the floor of the cave was covered with glistening green rock and shiny pebbles. He had no notion of the nature of the material apparently, but picked up some stones to take home, after the immemorial fashion of anyone at the seashore. The children of two generations used them as playthings. Such is the attraction of jade that you don't even have to know what you hold in your hand to value it.

Some fifty or sixty years after the sea lion hunt, a horticulturist, visiting the home of the hunter's grandchildren, admired the green pebbles and was given a handful. Subsequently they found their way to Will Ellington, who has always had an interest in such things. Dr. Rogers, head of the department of geology at Leland Stanford University, examined them and pronounced them nephrite jade of jewel quality.

The original sea lion hunter had never told anyone where he found his pebbles—if, indeed, he could remember. But Will Ellington decided to find out. He has an imagination like mine; it nags at him in low, well-modulated tones until he gets up and does something about it.

This particular nag worked away at Will for three years until one day, walking along the spectacular Monterey coast at low tide, he saw a mysterious, half-hidden opening into a dark rocky recess. It was such a pirate cave as any ten-year-old boy sees in his favorite dreams—and Will Ellington too. He went inside it, perfectly confident that he would find treasure of some sort. Robert Louis Stevenson spoke of certain coasts as being "set apart for shipwreck"—but this particular coast cave was obviously foreordained to contain treasure. Will was not disappointed. Within he found a palace of glistening jewels: water-washed stones of purest green jade; jade pebbles identical with the ancient artifacts of Mexico, the playthings of the hunter's children, and the boxful sent to me by my mysterious Monterey collector!

Although a wealth of material has already been removed from the Monterey cave, much still remains. I have not seen it, except through Will Ellington's eyes. I have referred to this find as "pebbles," simply because the stones are water-washed.

Actually, some of the pieces are in boulder form so huge that no one has been able to get them out—yet! There is at least one boulder which will weigh approximately ten tons, as smooth and glistening and rounded as though polished on a lapidary wheel.

This fabulous cave is toward the lower end of Monterey County. Approach must be made either by dropping straight down from the top of a cliff two hundred feet or more, or by sprinting along the beach from north or south at dead low tide. There is time, between ebb and flow, for no more than two hours' work each day, no matter which way you approach it. For the rest of each twenty-four hours, the cave is beneath the pounding waves of the Pacific. After a storm, even at low tide, a visitor might not see anything special; for at such times the gems are likely to be covered by gravel and sand.

Whether this particular cave is the actual source of the ancient Mexican carved pebbles I do not know. Since it exists so expertly hidden, others may also. There may be comparable natural jewel boxes on the coast of Mexico or Central America. Very likely there are. If not, our early Southwestern Indians might have used the pebbles as a medium of exchange.

But the Monterey pebbles are indisputably nephrite jade. Those I have worked with have been proved out, by nature herself in the water-polishing ages, to be exquisite jewel jade. Anyone who has ever tramped after jade to the remote, heel-blistering, back-breaking, nerve-straining, contrary spots which the stone chooses for its habitat must consider this Monterey pirate's cave a typical homesite for jade. Nature, even in her solemnest geologic dignity, is not above playing a joke. To polish a caveful of gems, and cover them with sea so that a man may view them just 120 minutes out of a day—and that only by running very fast—is just the kind of thing nature delights in. Simple grandeur, I suppose, could grow awfully dull without an amiable thrust now and then at the two-legged creatures who are forever invading her privacy.

8

Jade in Wyoming

BY FAR the most important finds of jade in the continental United States today are those of Wyoming, in the Lander area toward the Continental Divide. There seems a peculiar fitness in that jade should have chosen the Rocky Mountains for one of its great world homes. We call them the Rocky Mountains, but there is reason to believe that, in the language of the Indians who first knew them, their proper name was Mountains of the Shining Stones. I prefer to think so, at any rate—and that some of those shining stones which bedazzled the Indians were lustrous wind-polished jade!

As you view the tremendous panorama of Wyoming in your search for jade—or for any one of the many gem stones found there—you must be immediately aware that this is the perfect background for such adventure. Those heroic barren stretches, the uncluttered grandeur of mountain and plain somehow make you think that this was the last piece of earth fashioned by the hand of God—the Saturday-afternoon task. There you can see the pattern of the crust of earth—with all its riches—as if it had been left expressly for man to read. Though the pattern of the forming of jade has been there all the time, eloquently expressed, man has been very slow to read. He is beginning now, however; and the little city of Lander—from which many a jade adventure has begun—is fairly thrumming with the American version of "jade madness."

Jade in Wyoming

The tale of the finding of jade in Wyoming begins back in the early nineteen thirties with a man on a bicycle. His name, as Lander's rockhounds remember it, was Corbin, and he pedaled into Lander one summer day from Oregon, having braved the heights of the Continental Divide to look for agates in the Sweetwater River area about seventy-five miles south and east of Lander.

The Sweetwater agate was, and still is, a treasure for rock collectors, for it is a clear, hard, white agate interestingly patterned with fern traceries. As rockhound Corbin searched the river banks for agate, he picked up a greenish chip of rock idly, then stopped to look again.

"This," he said, "is jade, and I'd rather have a mine of this than a mine of gold!"

Corbin showed his piece of jade—it was an exceptionally dark clear green when cut and polished—to Biford Foster, a local collector of gems, so that he too would know what jade looked like and could keep his eyes open for more. But Corbin himself, with his lucky piece of jade and his Sweetwater agates, mounted his bicycle and rode off to the Oregon country and, so far as is known, never returned. But the search for jade in Wyoming began with this casual find.

Back in 1931, a sheepherder out on the range near Crooks' Mountain, south of Lander, brought in a sizable piece of dark green stone shot with quartz crystals which turned out to be jade. After its identification as nephrite he sold the piece to a museum. And Lander began to sit up and look about, scarcely knowing what to look for.

As I have pointed out, unless the prospector is lucky enough to discover a piece that is wind- or water-washed, jade seldom looks like jade. Normally covered with a surly rind of serpentine, asbestos, or other substance equally resistant, it only barely reveals faint streaks of green—or other jade color—beneath. Then, too, jade comes in so many colors that color is never a definitive test. Once you know the physical charac-

teristics of jade well, you can recognize it even in its hard rind.
But it takes some knowing. Prospectors in the Lander area
who have made the best finds of jade in float, figure that they've
passed over some of the prize boulders dozens of times without a second glance, until some trick of light or shadow has
encouraged them to investigate.

The next important find of jade in the Lander area was made
by Allan Branham, a grocer who had been a rock collector
since early days in Montana. In 1939, traveling in the Warm
Springs country near Granite Mountain, Branham found a
small piece of rich green jade. He sent it to a gem dealer in
California, who returned the piece with some scorn and doubt
of its being true nephrite.

Undaunted, Branham sent the piece to the Smithsonian
Institution, whose gemmologists promptly sent back word that
this was nephrite jade of exceptional gem quality. Half of
that small piece eventually went to the Gem Exchange in
Illinois, the other half to a collector in Oregon City. At both
markets the jade was hailed with delight. Both asked for quantities of the raw material.

Now this posed a real problem for the rockhounds of Wyoming. Whether quantities could be found no one of course
knew, but almost everyone in Lander started looking in earnest.
Branham gave up his grocery job to devote all his time to
searching for—and trading in—stones.

His experience is typical. He began looking in ever-widening
circles around Warm Springs, where he had made his original
find. After almost a year of search—a very lean year—he found
a fifty-pound chunk of nephrite on the prairie at the foot of
Crooks' Mountain. He believed reasonably enough that these
boulders must have fallen from the ledge of the mountain in
the process of erosion, and that the larger heavier stones would
be discovered nearer the base of the mountain. His later discoveries bore out the theory.

Enlisting the help of his wife—a sturdy and knowledgeable

rockhound in her own right—and his daughter, he searched throughout the summer months. In one summer he found about 2,000 pounds of jade in float on the rocky slopes of Crooks' Mountain. One boulder weighed 750 pounds, no mean engineering feat to transfer from the mountainside to a truck and thence over the prairie to the highway.

Up to the present time, the largest jade boulder that has been removed from this area weighs 2,495 pounds. It was discovered in the summer of 1940, and the Branhams had been searching earnestly—and lucklessly—all day. Marcia, the daughter, weary and discouraged with this endless hunt for jade, showed signs of wanting to call it a day.

"Marcia!" said her mother, "you're not really *looking!*" (Heresy to a rockhound.)

"O.K.," said Marcia, with the nonchalance of the younger generation and touching the toe of her boot to a giant boulder, "what's this, then?"

It was jade—pure nephrite jade of deep green! Nature has perhaps never been in a mellower mood than on that hot summer day! She proved not so amiable, however, when it came to getting the boulder out. I had the great thrill of seeing that tremendous chunk of jade just as it stood on the mountainside, and I had no sooner seen it than I determined that it properly belonged, just as it stood, in the great Chicago Natural History Museum—to join that classic and perhaps incomparable collection of jade pieces which, properly translated, tell a continuous story of man's search for and work with jade through centuries.

Because of its great value, it was important that the 1¼-ton stone of jade be brought from its hiding place as early as possible. Jade madness was well spread by 1940 in that area, and almost any clump of sagebrush might have concealed a man with a jade glint in his eye. Like conspirators, we discussed methods of getting the huge prize down the mountain. Finally we concluded that only a very large truck, a block and tackle, and the hard work of whatever man power we could muster among our friends would do the trick.

Getting a sizable truck over sand and sage was in itself a tremendous job. Securing tackle around the stone's generous midriff took more time than you can possibly imagine. Green jades worn for adornment were thought of as "feminine" jade in China. And if coyness is any longer a feminine attribute, this was certainly feminine jade. Solemn as the occasion was—and irritating too—I could not help thinking our 1¼-ton lady behaved very much as the fat lady of a circus might have done, winking behind her fan but stoutly declining to be carried inside the main tent!

Eventually she yielded to wile and brute strength—and was weighed out at exactly 2,495 pounds. In order to show the authorities at the Chicago museum just what it was that the Branhams had found, we had a small chunk knocked from the finger end of the boulder. I took it back to my workshop, made a few jewel pieces to be sent to the director of the museum and his wife, and the remainder went to the museum lapidary shop. After a long wait—or perhaps it merely seemed long, for I was so anxious about it—the report came in. Nephrite jade of excellent quality!

The Wyoming jade boulder was then accepted by the museum, presented with appropriate ceremonies in the presence of dignitaries and some charming little Chinese girls and boys who fingered the large jade chunk with incredulous eyes.

Since 1940, almost everyone in Lander—and some thousands of tourists—have been searching the area of Crooks' Mountain for jade in float. Some surprising finds have been made, too, by a wide variety of rockhounds: cowboys, sheepherders, remittance men, storekeepers, tourists on their way to Yellowstone Park. The chunks have varied from one to sixty pounds for the most part, though a few much larger finds have been made.

Thousands of acres of Wyoming are government sheep-grazing land. Mineral finds on top of the ground have been keepers for the lucky prospectors. Frequently there have been some rather spirited words spoken as to who the original finder might have been: families have camped with their jade stones overnight; feuds have developed; gunshot has been talked of; rumors have flown thicker than arrows. There has been such an air of conspiracy that any man's blood must quicken, as it surely did when gold was first discovered in the Klondike.

Most of the Wyoming jade in float has been found in close proximity to dikes in the mountain ranges. These dikes—giant vertical streaks of various kinds of stone, cutting the ranges—are thought to be merely the remnants of much larger dikes which, by erosion, have been worn down to their present state. The look of the jade boulders in float, often jagged and irregular, indicates that they were once a part of these solid wedges of rock thrown out by some great cataclysm when our Rocky Mountains were coming to birth.

The spectacular finds of Crooks' Mountain of course started a continuous trek through this section of the country. But after a while, the more businesslike searchers decided to comb the wide area to the other side of the highway, in what is known locally as Granite Mountain range (actually a part of the Rattlesnakes). No jade in float whatsoever was found there! Elusive, contrary jade! But the Granites had an even greater jade prize in store. For it was there that jade was first discovered in place, living jade in the very ribs of the Rockies.

Hart Robinson, a homesteader in the Granite Mountain area, filed and got a claim on a section of land where there were known to be star sapphires. Though of beautiful color, the sapphires turned out to be fractured so that the stars could not be polished satisfactorily. Robinson found, however, in addition to the sapphires, a black hard rock which he thought at first to be onyx. It was found in place, minable, fairly close to the surface. Analysis proved it to be nephrite, a good quantity of it of gem quality, all of lustrous black.

As sometimes happens in the prospecting business, however, the original claimant left the countryside and his mine very largely unexplored. Two other Lander men took up the claim and set a small mine into operation, perhaps the first jade mine in this country. Though the black jade from this mine has been pronounced extremely fine by authorities, it has not been mined or sold aggressively. Green jades have so long held the popular fancy that it is difficult to find a ready market for other colors, however beautiful.

Prospecting the Granite Mountain range in 1944, Branham made the next important find of jade in place. On a single semicircular hill his pickax uncovered two outcroppings of jade in a vein approximately 4 feet by 2½ feet. Coated thickly with white granite and fused to that material, this vein of jade is largely unexplored and unmined up to the present time. No one knows how much of it is of gem quality or how far the ledge may penetrate. It is fascinating to see this jade in place: the white granite with which it is coated is heavily blistered as though with terrific heat, and the jade vein itself appears to be twisted into the rock, much as if a cook had forced whipped cream through a pastry tube.

Such jade as has been taken from the Granite Mountain ledge has proved to possess about the same proportion of gem-quality jade as the boulders in float. All of it cut into so far has been of a greenish-brown color—not regarded as highly desirable. It is my belief, however, that if we developed a distinctly American color list for our native jades and called this one, say, wing-of-the-wild-turkey or sage-brush-dotted-with-snow, and if it should be worn with affection and pride by a few women of fashion, it might well come to be a very desirable color. I should call it a subtle color.

The important thing, at any rate, is that Wyoming, the country of the Mountains of the Shining Stones, was the first state in the Union to demonstrate to geologist and rockhound alike that jade does exist on this continent, not alone in float but in place, an integral part of our nation's stone structure.

Jade in Wyoming

Where did American jade come from? America, says Wyoming! And there is jade in place to convince the most skeptical!

What will undoubtedly prove to be an even richer find of Wyoming jade in place still holds most of its mystery. In the summer of 1944, a geologist from Missouri uncovered what is said to be a tremendous ledge of pure black jade. (Is it nephrite or chloromelanite, that fugitive wonder among all jades? We do not know!) He found it in the high, singing wilderness of the Wind River range, which few white men visit. It is said to be among the most beautiful and inaccessible spots on earth, at an altitude of 13,000 feet, where to walk at all is difficult without special training and where to dig out jade is work for heroes. The outcropping which he discovered is said to be a quarter of a mile long. It rises in hogback formation some twelve inches from the ground.

Despite the difficulties of getting jade out from this rugged country, the young geologist brought out about 100 pounds of the material, none of which I have had the privilege of seeing. Confiding his secret to one of Lander's prospectors, the young man left most of his find intact—and went off to the wars.

Since his original find, no one, so far as I know, has made a serious attempt to rediscover it or get any quantity of it out. It will require a special quality of vigor and enthusiasm and pioneering spirit to do so. Any jade brought out must be carried for at least thirty miles or so by horseback. A hundred pounds is probably the most a man and horse could bring out at any one time.

On numerous prospecting trips to Wyoming, I have cast a yearning eye toward that Wind River country. But so far I have contented myself with the findings lower down. If I had known of it twenty years ago—or if I were a young geologist from Missouri—I would be there now. So much of the secret as I know I give to you just as it came to me. If there is pioneering blood left in America—and I have no reason to doubt it—Wind River will one day echo to the ring of the prospector's pick. Meantime, she holds her secret safe. Black jade may be present there beyond the dreams of avarice. There is no need to put any limit on a rockhound's dream of the unknown!

More geological research and casual finds by rockhounds will undoubtedly uncover much more jade treasure in the Rocky Mountains. It is possible that the ledge in the Wind River country is the head of Rocky Mountain jade *in situ*. In places it probably vanishes beneath the granite; in others it may outcrop as in the Granite Mountain ledge.

In such areas as Beaver Divide, east of Lander, jade in place is to be found in a chain of disconnected boulders, coated with a thick layer of magnesium.

The Beaver Divide jade is being mined, and some interesting colors have been found ranging from pale gray to deep black. (I should like to see the American gray jades named in some such fashion as this: moonlight-on-the-Sweetwater, passenger pigeon, dust storm.)

Roughly, Wyoming's principal accessible jade fields to date, both for jade in float and in place, are restricted to a 200-mile area south and east of Lander. The area is circular.

Lucky finders of jade in float in the Lander area picked up from 7,000 to 8,000 pounds of the alluring stone in the summer of 1945. Much of it varied in color from light to very dark green. (The very light green jade of Wyoming most certainly ought to be called springtime-in-the-Rockies!) The material, of course, varies widely. Some of it is filled with small black particles that undercut as you work with it. When it is of gem quality, Wyoming jade is as fine, I believe, as any nephrite mined in the East in ancient times, a delight to the eye and to the fingers.

For a time, during the great jade rush of 1945, the jade talk of Lander was fantastic. Everyone was going to get rich quick, either by finding jade or by cutting and selling it. Unhappily—

or perhaps happily—no quick fortune has materialized out of the Wyoming jade finds. Jade is simply not that kind of gem and never has been. Elevated ideas of what a piece of uncut jade should bring have tobogganed in that area. Get-rich-quick prospectors are urged to turn their pickaxes to gold or some other mineral. The barest nodding acquaintance with Confucius should remind them that jade is not for man's material gain, but for the betterment of his immortal soul and the quickening of the spirit of adventure within him.

9

More Jade in California

UNTIL THE GREAT FINDS of jade in place in Wyoming, California had reported finds of jade only in float. Then, almost as though jealous of her old mining tradition, California came through with still another great discovery: jade in place near San Luis Obispo. That is, she halfway came through! Part of the mystery of a great minable vein of jade in what was once the Mohavia range is still unknown and untold. But I have jade from the diggings, and enough of the story so that adventurers and rockhounds may take up the scent.

The first whiff I had of this valuable quarry came from an unusual wind direction, not California at all, but New York City. A firm which manufactures and sells heavy chemicals wrote to ask if I would be interested in buying a quantity of jade. Their letter said candidly that they knew nothing of jade, but this material had been offered them in quantity, and they were putting forth every effort to sell it for their client.

They suggested sending samples, and nobody could resist an offer like that. I was skeptical, but willing to have a look. Up to that time, not a single source of jade that I knew of offered all the material I wanted. I supposed that the stone, therefore, whatever it was, could not possibly be jade. Surely anyone who had really uncovered a quantity of jade would not try to sell it through a chemical house.

Anyway, I asked for samples. And when they arrived, I found that they were flat pebbles, partially wind- and water-washed. Each pebble was of a different color; several were mottled. The material was nephrite jade. It bore some similarity to the jade pebbles of Monterey, yet the variety of colors and the lack of high water polish showed that they were not from Monterey. I couldn't imagine where the material might have originated, for it was unlike anything else I had seen from the United States. I wondered whether it might have come from Brazil, where some deposits of jade had been announced.

On inquiry, the chemical house gave me the information that the jade had been sent to them by a man living near San Luis Obispo, California. He replied to my urgent letter with the greatest courtesy and such details as he felt he could give without jeopardizing his own rights in the property. He also sent me a quantity of jade stones whose polishability and quality were excellent. The colors ranged from very pale green to jet black, some of the stones only an inch in diameter and about a half inch thick. Many were checked from the stress of being broken away from the lode *in situ*.

E. H. Atkinson—the miner and true rockhound who had found these beauties—reported that the pebbles were only that portion of a giant ledge which had broken away through erosion of one of the outcroppings. The depth and width and length of the whole ledge, so far as I know, are as yet unexplored, undetermined, and unknown.

Atkinson has not only found jade in place in California, but has given me his own story of the way he came upon it. In his spare time, for years, he said, he had been prospecting the Mt. Diablo district of California and finding deposits of minerals quite frequently in spots where they were not supposed to be. Among these, he had found manganese, feldspar, calcite, gold, and silver. When he came upon the broken-off jade pebbles, he wasn't sure just what these strangers to the Mt. Diablo district might be. He sent the material to the

California Department of Mines, and the authorities there pronounced it nephrite.

Knowing that his pebbles were nephrite, Atkinson searched further and at length found the outcroppings from which they came. He reported finding two ledges, running from two to six feet across and of an unknown depth. To one side of the ledges lies a massive deposit of talc; to the other, lies a deposit of serpentine, along with some basalt admixed with short asbestos. This is a fairly usual combination of minerals in the vicinity of jade. The interesting thing is that they should have been found in this particular region at all.

Atkinson explained the geology as he sees it in this way:

We have in San Luis Obispo County, an extension of the old Mohavia range. This is known to very few people. I did find verification of it, however, in an old report by a geologist of the University of California, who had made a survey of the Mohavia range. I found the most northerly outcropping of this old range at Dead Man's Flat in the Carissa Plains district. It consisted of a quartz hill about three miles long and 800 feet high. On the east side is sign of volcanic action, blow outs, rhyolite, etc.

On the west side, from the base of this hill to the ocean about 50 miles west, is the Franciscan Era overburden, which contains considerable serpentine. This old Mohavia range is covered over by the Franciscan formation for the entire distance from the Dead Man's Flat to south of the Tehachapi range, with the exception of a few basalt mounds in the South Carissa Plains district.

A few miles northwest from this hill at Dead Man's Flat occurs the broken up rubble formation of the Navajo grade district. Limited geological surveys which have been made of this district show that the broken formation was caused by the old Salina range butting against the Mohavia range and working alternately up and down, grinding the end of each range into a good imitation of a glacial deposit.

I agree with them on the grinding part of it, but not that the ranges met end to end. I haven't proved to my own satisfaction, but I feel very confident, that they are wrong in this contention.

More Jade in California

I believe that the old Salina range (which follows the same direction as the present Salinas River) butted into the Mohavia range at this point at about a 30-degree angle, and that the old Mohavia range continues on in a northwesterly direction and is covered over by the Franciscan overburden, which isn't very deep in some places.

Now here is a geologic point over which students may have to argue at some future date. If Atkinson is correct about the underlying Mohavia range—with its wealth of pre-Cambrian rocks, among them jade—he may very well have discovered one of the greatest of all the sources of jade on this continent, indeed on the earth. Meantime, he holds the honors, I believe, for having first reported jade *in situ* in California. So far he alone knows of the outcropping and has access to the jade of this ledge. Some of the material he has sent me is extremely beautiful; some of it is fractured and checked; much of it is in strange and unusual colors; but all of it is nephrite.

I have no notion how much jade will eventually be found in California, but I had scarcely made the acquaintance of San Luis Obispo jade when I met some jade from Placer County in the same state. It was sent to me by Mrs. Laurance LaKamp of Oakland, a descendant of three generations of miners.

The specimens she sent were deeply oxidized, almost unrecognizable as jade; so I was curious how she had made her designation.

Her reply indicated the genuine resourcefulness of a rockhound confronted with a rock he has never seen before. Mrs. LaKamp, her husband, her sister, and the sister's husband had discovered this particular rock when they were mining an old river channel in Placer County. As they mined, they were bothered by clogged sluice boxes and grizzlies. They particularly noticed the weight of one pesky kind of dark green rock.

But instead of throwing the rocks away, they were curious

enough to make the test for zinc ore, their first guess as to what the material might be. No, it wasn't zinc. They scoured their only reference, Peele's *Mining Engineer's Handbook*, for a description to fit the green stone, but found nothing remotely resembling it described therein.

Then someone sent them a mineralogy book for Christmas; and by careful reading of the text, eliminating one stone after another, they concluded that what they had found in the river bed was jadeite. Its hardness, determined by the scratch test, was under 7 (the hardness of jadeite) but very slightly under. They made a rough test for specific gravity and got 3.36 (the specific gravity of jadeite is 3.3). They got a fusibility of about $2\frac{1}{2}$, as they were able to fuse a small bead of the material onto a splinter with a gas flame. Fusing gave forth a sodium flame.

The LaKamps were careful workmen. They took an acetylene torch with an oxidizing flame to the material, and at terrific heat got a very clear bubbly glass slag with a slight green cast. With a reducing flame, they got a dark brown glass. Then, not satisfied, the LaKamps found a book on gem materials and made check tests for vesuvianite, grossularite, bowenite, amazonite, aventurine, sasserite, pectolite, and phrenite—all jade impostors. They satisfied themselves that their green rocks were none of these; and finally, after as thorough a going over as any rock ever had, they concluded that what they had was jade, either jadeite, or nephrite. They were right: the material is indeed jade.

Though the LaKamps so far have not found jade in Placer County *in situ*, they suppose that it may be found thus. In the Placer area, the country has been cut through by ancient river beds, by lava flows to a depth of several hundred feet. Present rivers, they believe, have cut down through one of the ancient channels to scatter what loose jade lies there in float.

The persistence of these seekers after jade interested me as much as the jade they had found; so in 1945 on a trip to California, I called on them. They had virtually given up their mining operations during the war, for the menfolk of the family had gone into machine-tool shops to help make the devices for victory.

But every once in a while, they told me, the call of their mining blood got too strong. So they drove to the mountains on week-end trips, to discover a likely spot to begin prospecting in earnest after the war.

While they were prospecting for pay dirt in a placer region, they discovered some heavy boulders of jade, material identical with the smaller pieces which they had so painstakingly classified with their miner's tests.

Behind the modest bungalow where these adventurous people lived were several thousand pounds of Placer County jade. They had also set up a most adequate lapidary shop, with a twenty-inch diamond saw. Much of the stone which they had already sliced was gem material of outstanding merit, in colors differing from any other I have seen. Especially beautiful was one piece of transparent orange-bronze, shading to light yellow. Oddly enough, in all the material they had behind the house, there was no piece of typical green jade. Of course, the LaKamps had made no particular effort to find green jade or to choose colors before they brought the material in. It would have been very difficult to do so anyhow, for the thick skin or rind of jade would have obscured the true color.

As we fell to swapping rockhound yarns, the LaKamps and I, I discovered still other evidence that the first Chinese who came to California were well aware of the jade on this continent. They merely kept the information to themselves, quite wisely.

It seems that this particular placer area was mined for many years by a group of Chinese. They worked with primitive tools and by methods which ensured that every foot of the gravel would be carefully panned.

Almost up to the beginning of the Second World War, Chinese had mined this area. When they departed, they left a distinct line indicating just how far the ground had been worked. This is the curious thing: in the area worked by the Chinese, not so much as a nodule of jade was found, but scattered throughout the area still unworked in the same territory, there were jade boulders in quantity, both upon the surface and below the ground.

It may be that for many years the search for gold had been merely the polite pretext for a search of far greater importance to the Chinese miners: the search for jade. It is also perfectly possible that quantities of American jade from Placer County were quietly moving back to China, there to be cut and carved and mounted and sold to such traveling Americans as appreciated the beauty of this mystic gem! The prophet is not without honor!

10

Jade Is Where You Find It!

IT WILL SURPRISE no rockhound—and ought not surprise anybody—that once jade was found and undeniably
classified as nephrite in America, it began to be found almost everywhere. At least, it was reported everywhere. Almost
anyone uncovering a green rock from here to the Arctic Circle
believed himself the discoverer of a piece of jewel jade.

Now jade is not that kind of rock, either: it is not found
everywhere and will not be! Much beautiful green nonjade
material appears throughout the great mountains of our West.
If the finder discovers that what he has is not truly jade, that
should in nowise discourage him about further search or from
taking joy in cutting and polishing what he has.

Since the public stir caused by the finding of jade in both
Alaska and Wyoming, hundreds of people have sent samples
of various green stone to me. Much of it, of course, has proved
to be nonjade material; some of it has been beautiful; and I
have ignored none of it. It isn't in my nature to leave any
really beautiful stone uncut.

Some of the material is on the border line between nephrite
—and something else. I say it is on the border line, though of
course a stone is either jade or it isn't. But the border-line cases
are the stones having some of the qualities of nephrite, being
deficient in one or two. Others that I have received are con-
troversial, pronounced nephrite by some jewel experts and

[69]

something else by others. There are rather fine distinctions separating the true from the false, at times, as in other departments of human affairs.

One of the great question marks in the jade search is Idaho. I have always felt that jade *ought* to be present in that state: its rock formations suggest a splendid background for jade. I have done some assiduous prospecting out there; I like the state anyhow; and a piece of really good Idaho landscape or ten inches of really good Idaho trout are worth a day's hard work any time.

I have heard lots of rumors of jade in Idaho, but I had never been able to localize those rumors until one day I received something much better: a box of stone from a rockhound at Hansen, Idaho. His letter called the stone nephrite. The color of the Hansen pieces was exquisite—transparent blue-green, such as the Chinese delighted in. But here was a strange thing: the material was laminated, in minute thin layers. Now lamination is not a physical characteristic of either jadeite or nephrite. I concluded that this Idaho stone could not be jade, though it was extremely hard and had the specific gravity of jadeite. Intrinsically the material was so beautiful that I did some work on it at the shop. And I tried to find out more about it. My Hansen correspondent said—and this didn't surprise me a bit—that it came from a quite inaccessible mountain region; that it could be mined for only about a month in midsummer because of the heavy snows; and that the state geologist had pronounced the stone jade. The material was found in place, in many and varied colors. If I liked, more would be sent me.

Finally about fifty pounds of this finely laminated material arrived. I took it to the workshop with all possible speed and have seldom had a more rewarding evening's work. When I had finished, I had gem stones of many magnificent colors: emerald green, rose pink, and in-between shades to rival the rainbow. It behaved like jade beneath the saw and the polishing wheels; its polish was very high; its refraction like that of nephrite. But it was laminated. I sent samples of the material to two geological experts. One reported that it was a new combination of minerals, but certainly neither nephrite nor jadeite. The other said it was nephrite.

About the time these reports were coming back, one of our Kraft boys in service sent me a box of rough jade from Burma. That jade had been definitely called jadeite. It had every characteristic of jade and responded to all the tests, except one: this rough jade from Burma was finely laminated.

I am not prepared to say whether this infinitely various and beautiful stone from Idaho is or isn't jade. I will let the mineralogists make the final decision. But if it is not, it well deserves to be, and maybe that is enough.

In the stir caused by jade discoveries, there is much of the bustle, intrigue, mystery, conniving, chicanery, and plain downright thievery associated with any great mineral discovery. The gold rush of '49 brought on such a storm of this kind of thing that we are only now beginning to see it for the picturesque romance which, among other things, it was. Jade searchers, like other prospectors, are an entertaining and unusual lot. They have their idiosyncrasies like other people, and being lonelier than most, probably have even more spectacular dreams than the mine-run. I have known men who would pan for thirty years, scarcely more than seeing gold, firm in their faith that the next wash would show just what they were looking for.

No one has ever written a proper book about what it is that makes a prospector tick. I wish someone would. I believe he has an inward quality, quite apart from lust for gold, that would greatly profit an average shoe clerk or public accountant or captain of industry or statesman.

Though I do not know him—if indeed he is still alive—I recount part of a Wyoming prospector's tale because I think it shows something about the indomitable dream of prospectors. He claims to have found jade of rare purple and pink and light green shades in the great fossil country near Kemmerer, Wyoming. I know this country well and have taken many a fossil fish from those quiet once-ocean beds, but I have never come upon any jade out that way—possibly because I have not looked hard enough.

At any rate, I had heard a number of rumors about the finding of jade near Kemmerer. Denials and affirmations followed close upon one another. I wrote to the prospector who had made the first claim, and received a long letter from him quoting prices. These were rather high, but if, as he said, his jade was of purple and pink, what might it not be worth? I ordered some.

When the material from Kemmerer arrived I found, to my regret, that it was all a sort of pale gray, with the inclusion of other more or less drab colors—one of them almost amber. (One could call it Brontosaurus-brown jade, I suppose, in honor of the fossil relic of that curious beast found in the general area.) The pieces were rather badly checked from sledging when broken from the ledge. Then, too, at some millions-of-ages-ago time, the deposit must have been brecciated by nature. Breaks in the body of the stone had been healed in with what appeared to be agate.

Not purple nor pink nor green but only slightly relieved gray as the material was, I cut into it anyway. I polished some round and oval cabochons and, somewhat to my surprise, there was real beauty in the material; not purple beauty but gray beauty.

I wrote again for more material and suggested other colors, but my prospector friend did not reply. His first letter had told a somewhat lurid tale: someone had burned his cabin, killed his horse, and would go to any lengths to get him out of the country. His jade was so beautiful, he said, so various and so valuable that there were desperadoes from many places prepared to do him in for the secret of its source.

But I have had no further word and received no further

material from this source. The strange gray material has the hardness and the toughness of nephrite. It polishes brilliantly. In its own curious way it is beautiful. I wish I might have all the colors the prospector claimed to have found. I hope for his sake—and for the dream which undoubtedly warmed him many a cold, lonely Wyoming night—that he did find jade of purple and red and yellow. If this neutral gray stone which he sent me is all that he found, then I hope that he lives—or died— still seeing through some specially benign desert mirage the whole spectrum in his monotone jade.

11

Shoptalk

THERE ARE essentially two kinds of people for whom stones are the perfect hobby: one kind are by nature rockhounds, principally interested in the search for stones; the others are amateur "laps" whose principal interest is in working with stones—and never mind who found them. The workshop is the nub of their interest: cutting, polishing, designing jewelry, setting stones. Both occupations are fascinating beyond comparison.

Now there is another kind of hobbyist in the field, a man who is both rockhound and amateur lap. I am that kind. Logically, I suppose, a man who is both rockhound and amateur lap should expect himself to be called a "lap dog." But this is a libel which no combination rockhound and lap will take sitting down.

Your true rockhound obviously can have none of the characteristics of a house critter. He needs to be particularly rugged and enduring. He must be adventurous, pioneering, incurably curious, tireless. He must have strong arches, stout boots, and a structure of spirit to match them. Deplorably, perhaps, he should be a little stubborn. He should also be uncomplaining, adaptable, subject to sudden inspirations, capable of the discoverer's and the child's delight. He should be indifferent to discouragement and the comments of his neighbors as he starts off on some wild-goose chase.

He must have the young man's ability to sleep beneath the stars with uncomplaining bones. He must have the pioneer's capacity for wearing heavy clothing and carrying heavy packs without flinching. He ought to have a good appetite for the most casual kinds of picnics, and develop a fondness for canned beans. He ought to have a lot of friends, especially in remote rock-hunting country, people who know where they're going, what they expect to find when they get there, and, most important of all, how to get home again after they've found it. This is the kind of friends to have in any case, and one cannot begin accumulating them too early.

Most stones worth looking for—and of jade this is particularly true—are found in inconceivably awkward places. High, cold, hazardous, lonely spots on the earth's surface claim jade for their own: you have to love jade genuinely to look for it.

You must also love it a lot to work with it in a lapidary shop. There is nothing easy about either the search or the working with it after you've found it. But anyone with the courage to seek and find it probably has the qualities necessary for working with it in the shop thereafter. Such work requires a great many of the same qualities, plus a certain sensitivity in the fingers.

That is why so much of this book has been spent describing the virtues of one particular stone and the peculiar excitement of finding it. And it is why I have spent so little time—none at all really—describing methods of working jade in the shop.

This will perhaps prove a disappointment to some of my lap friends who know me chiefly in the shop and through my work there. Amateur laps are eternally wanting to know how other laps work, what saws and wheels and buffers and abrasives and polishing compounds they use. Swapping such information is one of the delights of lapidary work. And for those who seriously wish to pursue the art in the workshop, there are excellent references and much practical help in the bibliography appended to this volume.

But learning to work with stones, and especially with jade, is a thing that a man must learn for himself in a shop. If he truly loves the material in which he works, he will do so. Talk is all very well, but you will never learn to handle jade until you get it into a shop, cut into it with a diamond saw, and proceed from there to develop a technique of your own. There are many ways of working with the material satisfactorily, some better than others.

In addition to skill, the amateur lap will need patience, resourcefulness, imagination, and an almost complete disregard for passing hours. There has never been a wasted moment in a lapidary shop so far as I know, however faulty the finished pieces which came out of the work. Anything you learn about the nature of stones as you work with them—and about yourself as a workman during the process—is knowledge gained and adventure sustained.

I will not detract from that essentially personal delight in discovery for any man by describing here in detail how I work with jade. I would like merely to invite you to set up shop and see for yourself. Whatever you expect of that experience, your ultimate discoveries are bound to be different—and satisfactory beyond anything you can hope.

Although finding and working the material itself is the chief satisfaction of rockhound and lap, there is no small joy, when that is done, in contemplating the results of your labor. To collect finished pieces and make a meaningful pattern out of them (and by meaningful I refer principally to a pattern which has significance and beauty for the workman himself) is a source of endless delight.

If the hobbyist has also a zeal for arrangement and selection, he may have a jewel case filled with treasure which no mere collector of other people's handiwork can hope to obtain. For along with the jewels which represent the very highest skill he has been capable of, he will have a collection of his own favorite memories, dreams, and ambitions. Each showpiece will represent the work of his own hands; each will be a yardstick of how nearly his labors approached his aspirations.

Every improvement in the technique of turning a gem into a jewel is an inch added to a special kind of stature. To be able to observe one's own growth in this particular would, you might suppose, give a man a dizzying sense of pride. On the contrary, any exultation of an amateur lap is likely to be of the humblest sort: there is so much yet to be done; there are so many ways of doing things; and tomorrow always remains a day for making the more perfect jewel.

I call my collection of finished jade pieces—the few that I have kept for my own soul's satisfaction out of thousands—Jade of Many Colors. It is literally that, for within its rows and niches are native American jades of more than 200 distinct colors and variations of shade. By tomorrow I shall have 300. On a par with his delight in the specimens he keeps to warm his soul, is the lap's pleasure in giving the product of his hands as widely and wisely as possible. To know that some small piece of the earth's mystery—cut and polished and set, as eloquent as you can make it—may be telling its story to people who love stones in other parts of the world is a most satisfying reward to the artisan.

For both rockhound and amateur lap, any new mineral discovery offers a thrill comparable with sighting new land. One would be most remiss if he did not shout out the news of such discovery. The purpose of this book is to point to the principal areas of present jade discovery: the great fields of Alaska, California, Wyoming, and the question-mark finds in other places. Like the pirate's or early miner's record, it points you to where true treasure lies, but leaves you to find the pathways there by yourself.

In due time—but not soon, I hope, for the sake of rockhounds to come after—all the jade of this continent will be found, recorded, mapped, and geologically classified. Skilled lapidaries, here and abroad, will have learned to work with it so skillfully and well that jewelry of jade—in a fascinating American color, springtime-in-the-Rockies or snow-over-the-Great-Divide—may well be the fashion pieces of the future. If we develop sufficient skill, jade might well be the medium for a great flowering of art and culture, as it was so long ago in an older, and in many ways wiser, civilization than our own.

Whether these things come to be or not, the jade in which such an art might be wrought is here in our hills and streams. The mystery begins to unfold. Finding jade anywhere is one of the most exciting adventures on earth; working with it successfully is one of the deep personal gratifications of an adventurous spirit.

It will be noted that this volume is in nowise a scientific work. For the most part, the persons who have uncovered the all-but-lost trail of jade on the American continent have been not geologists nor scientists at all, but everyday men of ordinary stations and walks of life. They have had only one characteristic in common: they have been rockhounds.

To my mind this is as it should be. The geologist and the archaeologist have their own special kind of fun and reward in their researches. As they help to build the half-hidden story of the world, they make a vast and incalculable contribution to living. But they do not have all the fun nor make the sole contribution.

The everyday man, the man without a great deal of special knowledge or scientific information at his disposal to start with, has also in every field uncovered much of great interest and often of great significance. It is so with rockhounds of every degree and shade of authoritative knowledge. Like pioneers breaking any frontier, they are endowed with different talents and characters and abilities, but they all make their mark in the wilderness.

Best of all, what the everyday man discovers, if he searches for and finds and works in beautiful stones, is a new continent seen for the first time by his eyes alone. It is a land as bright and fair, as filled with treasure and promise as ever it seemed to Americus Vespucius. On our rapidly contracting globe, to find a whole new world of your own is surely glory enough for any man.

BIBLIOGRAPHY

The Curious Lore of Precious Stones, by George Frederick Kunz, Philadelphia, J. B. Lippincott Company, 1913; Garden City, New York, Blue Ribbon Books, Inc., 1938.

Jade: A Study in Chinese Archaeology and Religion, by Berthold Laufer, Chicago, R. R. Donnelley & Sons Company, February, 1912.

Story of the Gems, by Herbert P. Whitlock, New York, Emerson, 1936; Garden City, New York, Garden City Publishing Company, Inc., 1940.

Precious Stones, by S. N. Burnham, Boston, Bradley Whidden, 1886.

Gems and Gem Materials, by Edward Henry Kraus and Chester Baker Slawson, New York and London, McGraw-Hill Book Company, Inc., 1941.

Jade Lore, by John Goette, New York, Reynal & Hitchcock, Inc., a John Day book, 1937.

Chinese Jade, by Frank Davis, London, The Commodore Press, Ltd., 1944.

Revised Lapidary Handbook, by J. Harry Howard, 504 Crescent Ave., Greenville, S. C., J. Harry Howard, 1946.

Art of Gem Cutting, by H. C. Dake and Richard Pearl, Portland, Oregon, The Mineralogist Publishing Co., third edition, 1946.

The Mineralogist Magazine (monthly publication), 329 S.E. 32nd Ave., Portland, Oregon.

"Jade Hunt," by A. Livingston Gump as told to Frank Taylor (first appeared in *The Saturday Evening Post* of June 12, 1937), San Francisco, H. S. Crocker Co. Inc.

PRODUCTION NOTES

DESIGNER: Maurice Serle Kaplan

TYPES: Linotype *Electra* and Bauer *Weiss*

TYPESETTING AND ELECTROTYPING: J. S. Cushing Co.

PRINTING AND BINDING: The Plimpton Press

FRONTISPIECE: Plates by Eagle Engraving Co. Printed by Marbridge Printing Co.